About this book

Mega English offers practice in literacy skills as described in the guidelines for the National Literacy Strategy. The book reflects the content of the National Curriculum in England and Wales and the 5-14 English Language programme in Scotland.

The book is divided into three sections. Many skills overlap these divisions. We recommend that your child works through the book in the given order. Repetition and practice will help build skills and confidence.

Answers appear on pages 122-128, so that either you or your child can check and mark the work.

How to help your child

Let your child decide how long they want to work on the book. Give lots of encouragement and praise for effort.

Instructions are written clearly and simply, but you may need to look through the activities and explain what your child is being asked to do. If your child has problems with a type of activity, talk about it together and try to help. You may need to discuss it with your child's class teacher.

About the author

Nicola Morgan is an experienced literacy teacher and the author of more than 50 educational books.

Written by Nicola Morgan
Illustrations by James Robins

EGMONT

We bring stories to life

First published in Great Britain in 2002 by Egmont UK Limited
239 Kensington High Street, London W8 6SA
Published in this edition in 2011
© 2011 Egmont UK Limited

ISBN 978 1 4052 5897 5
1 3 5 7 9 10 8 6 4 2
Printed in Italy

2 Contents

Contents

WRITING COMPOSITION

A noun is a thing, person, place or idea.
Ordinary nouns are called **common nouns.**
Special nouns are called **proper nouns.**
They have a capital letter at the beginning.
Names of people, cities, towns, countries, continents, months, and days of the week are all proper nouns.

Example:
I have underlined common nouns and put a circle round proper nouns.
Paris is the capital city of France. It has wide streets with expensive shops and cafes selling crusty bread. The Eiffel Tower is one of the strangest buildings in the world and can be seen for miles.

Underline the common nouns and circle the proper nouns:

Japan is a rich country in Asia. Its capital city is called Tokyo. Japan has modern factories, which make machines to sell all over the world. Many televisions, washing machines, cameras, computers and cars come from Japan. Rice is very important but farmers also grow wheat, barley and soya. There are Japanese restaurants in many countries, where you can taste their dishes of raw fish and beautifully shaped vegetables.

A **collective noun** is a word that we use for a group of other nouns.

Examples:

a *crowd* of people   a *family*   a *pack* of wolves

a *herd* of cows   a *shoal* of fish   a *column* of numbers

a *pride* of lions   a *herd* of elephants   a *gaggle* of geese

Circle the collective nouns:

apple	bunch
swarm	pack
bread	group
herd	shoal
flock	soup
team	comma

Put the correct collective noun in each space:

a _____ of wolves

a _____ of bananas

a _____ of bees

a _____ of footballers

a _____ of birds

Make up your own collective noun for:

a _____ of scarecrows   a _____ of homework

a _____ of dirty plates   a _____ of teachers

Singular means 'one thing'. **Plural** means 'more than one'.
Nouns have different ways of showing whether they are singular or plural.
Most nouns just add **s**, like cat/cats.
If the plural ending sounds like 'iz', you should add *es*, like *buses*. Words that end in *o*, usually add *es*. Some words don't change at all, like *sheep* and *trousers*.

Examples:

Singular	Plural
pin	pin**s**
fox	fox**es**
hero	hero**es**

ill in these spaces:

Singular	Plural
ship	_____
bush	_____
_____	tomatoes
sheep	_____

Write the plural instead of each underlined noun:

I saw <u>a cat</u> eat <u>an ice cream</u> while waiting for <u>a bus</u>.

_____

Have you ever seen <u>a potato</u> with <u>an eye</u> that blinked?

_____

The <u>burglar</u> hid the <u>watch</u> behind <u>a bush</u>.

_____

She picked up the <u>lamb</u> and the <u>sheep</u> followed her home.

_____

Nouns ending in **f** or **fe** usually change to **ves**,
like hoo**f** – hoo**ves** and kni**fe** – kni**ves**.
(But **ff** just adds **s**, like sni**ff** – sni**ffs**.)
Some nouns change completely, like child – children.

Examples:

Singular	Plural
woman	women
half	halves
wife	wives
staff	staffs

Fill in these spaces:

Singular	Plural
child	_____
calf	_____
_____	men
loaf	_____
_____	huffs

Write the plural of each underlined noun:

The <u>wolf</u> took a huge <u>puff</u> but couldn't blow the <u>house</u> down.

_____

The <u>man</u> needed a hot <u>knife</u> to fit <u>a shoe</u> to the pony's <u>hoof</u>.

_____

I put my <u>foot</u> in my <u>trousers</u> and caught my <u>toe</u> on the <u>button</u>.

_____

Pronouns

We use a pronoun instead of a noun. We use them so that we don't have to repeat the same noun lots of times. But be careful to make sure that the reader will know what each pronoun stands for.

Here are some pronouns: **he   she   it   we   you   they**
These are called **personal pronouns** – they stand for a person or thing.

Example:

John sat down and opened the parcel. It looked very interesting.
This is fine, because we know that It means the parcel.

Tony and Jack came into the room. Sarah looked at him crossly.
This is not fine, because we don't know whether him means Tony or Jack.

In this story, write a pronoun to replace each underlined noun:

Walking along my street, I saw an old lady. <u>The old lady</u> looked in pain.

_____

I asked <u>the old lady</u> if I could do anything to help. <u>The old lady</u> asked me to

_____

phone her son. I phoned <u>her son</u> and <u>her son</u> asked me where she was.

_____

I told <u>her son</u> that <u>his mother</u> was by the supermarket. <u>The supermarket</u> was the

_____

one the <u>old lady</u> always went to so <u>the son</u> knew where to find <u>the old lady</u>.

_____

Some pronouns are called **possessive pronouns.**
They show that something belongs to a person or thing.
Here are some:

my mine your yours his her hers their theirs our ours

Example:

Mrs Bond put a label on **her** cake to show that it was **hers**.

If we didn't use these possessive pronouns, we would have to say:

Mrs Bond put a label on **Mrs Bond's** cake to show that it was **Mrs Bond's**!

Put a possessive pronoun in each space:

1. Jack knew that the bag was _____ because it had _____ books in it.

2. The queen didn't like _____ stepdaughter, because she was so pretty.

3. The teams had brought _____ mascots to the competition.

4. We have put a pond in _____ garden.

5. Sally often wears my clothes, just because she's _____ younger sister.

6. Please give it back to me – it's _____!

7. Please put _____ own clothes away.

Top tip:

Don't get muddled with their and there. *Their* is the possessive pronoun. It only means *belonging to them.*

Verbs tell us what is happening. They are 'doing' words.
In a sentence, they tell us what a noun is doing, thinking or feeling.
Every sentence must have a verb, otherwise it would not make sense.

Example: *He down the street.*
There is no verb so it doesn't mean anything.
We could choose *ran, walked, strolled, charged, drove* or anything that makes sense.
When you write, choose the best verb to tell the story **you** want.

Choose any verbs you like to make these into good sentences:
The first one has been done for you.

strolled   *burying*
I ∧ along the beach ∧ my toes in the sand.

The rain ∧ my face and the wind ∧ in my ear.

Three dogs ∧ round the corner. I ∧ with fright.

The snake ∧ along the ground and ∧ into a hole.

The terrified mouse ∧ into its hole when the cat ∧ .

I ∧ up a tree to ∧ from the fierce dog.

When we write, we need to think about the words we use. Different verbs can give a very different meaning to a sentence. By choosing carefully, you can make sure the reader gets the idea you want.

Example:

Here are some words that mean eat:

eat   chew   gobble

munch   consume   nibble

He nibbled his food. She gobbled her meal.

What is different about the way they ate? Perhaps the boy didn't like his food, or wasn't hungry. But the girl liked the food, didn't she? She sounds hungry!
That's why verbs are so important. They tell the story.

Top tip:

Use a thesaurus to help you find new words.

Choose a verb to fill each space.

screamed   shouted   replied   asked   whispered

1. I _____ to my mum that tea was ready.

2. She _____ that she would be down soon.

3. My sister _____ 'What's for tea?'

4. I _____ that it was cabbage pie.

5. She _____ 'I hate cabbage!'

Can you think of five words to use instead of **go**?

_____

_____

_____

_____

_____

Verbs - tenses

Verbs have different endings to tell us **when** something happened.
Something that is **happening now** is in the **present tense**.
Something that **has happened** is in the **past tense**.
Something that is going to **happen later** is in the **future tense**.

Example:

1. The sun will shine tomorrow. (future)
2. The sun is shining today.   (present)
3. The sun shone yesterday.   (past)

Say whether each verb is present, past or future:

1. She <u>ran</u> to the water and <u>screamed</u> at the coldness. _____ _____

2. I <u>will do</u> my homework later. _____

3. My leg <u>hurts</u> when I <u>touch</u> it. _____ _____

4. I <u>am watching</u> television so I <u>can't come</u> to the phone. _____ _____

5. They <u>went</u> to Spain last year. _____

6. Whenever it <u>rains</u> I <u>love</u> the smell of it. _____ _____

7. Alice <u>will shrink</u> because she <u>has drunk</u> the potion. _____ _____

When verbs change tense, two things can happen.

The ending of the verb may change: jump, jump**s**, jump**ed**, jump**ing**.

A small word might go in front of it: **am** jumping, **will** jump.

These small words are part of the verb **to be**.

Here they are: *am, are, is, will, was, were*

We can change a sentence into the past tense.

Example:

I jump on the bike and cycle away.

I jumped on the bike and cycled away.

Turn these into the past tense:

1. She hops faster than her brother but he jumps higher.

_____

2. I want to go out.

_____

3. Jody laughs as she looks down at her filthy clothes.

_____

4. As we walk along the beach, the sea is lapping at our feet.

_____

What is the past tense of these verbs?

talk	trickle	hope	climb	want	allow	die
_____	_____	_____	_____	_____	_____	_____

Verbs - more about tenses

We usually use the past tense for writing stories.
Stories are often about things that have already happened.
There are different types of past tense:

I was jumping   I jumped   I have jumped   I had jumped

Example:

I <u>was waiting</u> at the park for an hour. My fingers <u>turned</u> blue with cold.
I <u>decided</u> that you had gone home. My mum <u>said</u>, 'Your fingers <u>have turned</u> blue!' I <u>had noticed</u> that myself.

Turn the underlined verbs in this story into the past tense:

I <u>am wandering</u> along the busy pavement. Suddenly, a girl <u>looks</u> at me and

_____

screams. Everyone <u>starts</u> looking at me. The girl's friends <u>are screaming</u>, but

_____

they <u>don't seem</u> frightened, just excited. In fact, they <u>start</u> touching me.

_____

What <u>is happening</u>? 'Oh Lee, Lee!' they <u>are shouting</u>. Then I <u>realise</u>: they

_____

<u>believe</u> I <u>am</u> a famous popstar.

_____

Sometimes the ending changes because of the tense.

But it can also change because of the **person.**

We talk about **1st, 2nd and 3rd person, singular and plural.**

	Singular	**Plural**
1st person	**I** like	**we** like
2nd person	**you** like	**you** like
3rd person	**he, she, it** likes	**they** like

Which ending was different?

You might be asked to write 'in the 1st person'.

Then you would use I or we for your story.

Example:

Change these into the first person singular.

They were walking – I was walking.

He jumps – I jump.

It's very easy – just remember what 1st, 2nd and 3rd person mean, in singular and plural.

Turn these into the
1st person plural:

He climbed Mount Everest.

_____

They helped at the school play.

_____

I am going to Spain next year.

_____

Turn these into the
2nd person singular:

He shouldn't have done that.

_____

I am good at football.

_____

I was happy to go home.

_____

More about tenses

You already know how verbs can be **present, past or future tense.**
Even if a story is in the past, there may be some sentences which need to be in the future or the present. But be careful to choose the correct one in each case.

Example: I walked boldly onto the running track. I knew I would win this race. I always feel confident before a race.

The story is set in the past but you can also see a future verb and a present verb. Think about how the meaning would change if they were all past tense.

Fill the gaps in this story and say whether the verb you have written is past, present or future tense:

AVALANCHE HORROR	Which tense?
A British family _____ a lucky escape in the Alps when an avalanche _____ them by 20 metres. Dan and Sue Bright, with Billy (8) and Jemma (10), _____ discussing where they were going to ski next, when they _____ an enormous roaring noise and tons of snow _____ past. 'We _____ here every year,' _____ Dan Bright, 'and we have never experienced anything like this. We _____ certainly come back though, as it _____ such a beautiful place. We _____ skiing and this_____ put us off.'	

The normal past tense ending for a verb is **-ed**. But lots of verbs have completely different endings. These are called **irregular verbs**, meaning that they don't follow a pattern. You probably know most of them.

Example:

I write to my aunt each month. (present)

I wrote to my aunt last week. (past)

Each bracket contains a verb in the present tense. All these verbs are irregular. In each space, put the same verb in the past tense:

1. Henry VIII _____ (has) six wives.

2. lorence Nightingale _____ (is) the first professional nurse.

3. The Duke of Wellington _____ (fights) Napoleon.

4. Wellington _____ (wins) the battle of Waterloo.

5. Poor children in the 19th century _____ (do) not go to school.

6. Missionaries _____ (teach) people about Christianity.

7. Alexander the Great _____ (thinks) he _____ (can) rule the world.

Write the past tense of these irregular verbs:

8. steal _____   9. eat _____   10. catch _____

11. make _____   12. buy _____   13. speak _____

14. hear _____   15. swim _____   16. run _____

Powerful verbs

Your writing will be better if you take care to choose the best verb you can think of. Although some verbs may be useful because they can be used in many different ways, other verbs may be *better* because they have *exactly* the right meaning and paint a stronger picture for the reader.

Example:

Fire came out of the beast's nostrils. Fire (blazed) out of the beast's nostrils.

She came into the room. She (crept) into the room.

The circled verbs are much more powerful because they give the reader a much clearer and more lively image. The verb 'came' is useful but can be boring.

Replace each underlined verb with the best verb from the list below. Or perhaps you could think of even better verbs yourself:

slumped   shot limped   lumbered   trickled   yelled

1. The elephant <u>went</u> down the road, holding all the traffic up. _____

2. Blood <u>came</u> from the cut on her leg. _____

3. 'I've told you three times not to do that!' <u>said</u> my Mum. _____

4. She <u>walked</u> slowly off the pitch, leaning on her hockey stick. _____

5. He was so tired that he <u>sat</u> on a chair. _____

6. The cat <u>came</u> out of the hole like lightning. _____

It's not just a matter of choosing a more powerful verb –
you need to choose exactly the right one for the meaning you want.

Example:

She came into the room. (We can't tell how she did it.)
She crept into the room. (She did it quietly, trying not to be noticed.)
She burst into the room. (She did it noisily and fast.)
She slunk into the room. (She did it quietly, and perhaps guiltily.)

I have underlined the weak verbs again.
For each, I have given you choices of stronger verbs.
Choose one and circle it; then write something to
explain what you want the reader to think. I've done
the first one for you.

Top tip:
Always try to think of
a better verb than
got or get.

1. Blood came from his nose. (trickled, flooded, spouted, dripped)

   There was a lot of blood pouring out.

2. She walked down the street. (hobbled, strolled, strode, marched)

   _____

3. 'Please,' said Sorghal. (whispered, begged, screamed, muttered)

   _____

4. I sat on the bench. (sprawled, relaxed, perched, slumped)

   _____

5. He came towards me. (lunged, rushed, flew, strolled)

   _____

6. I got up from the floor. (scrambled, forced myself, leapt, struggled)

   _____

Adjectives are describing words. They help stories come alive. Choosing the best adjectives is very important.

Example:

My parents gave me a bike. It had wheels and a frame. There were gears and a bell. There were tyres on the wheels and there was a saddle. Can you picture that bike clearly? No! We need adjectives, like this:

My parents gave me a beautiful brand-new bike. I loved its shiny silver wheels and red and black frame. Eighteen gears and tyres as thick as a strong man's arm made this the bike of my dreams.

Choose adjectives to improve this story.
Use the ones below, or choose your own:

The _____ waves were crashing on the _____ beach. They made

a _____ noise like a _____ animal roaring in the distance. In the

_____ sky the _____ clouds were gathering and I could see that

a _____ storm was on its way. As I started to go home, the first

_____ drops of _____ rain landed on my face.

fierce	huge	angry	frightening	grey	black	gloomy
dark	terrible	cold	beating	thick	wild	

When you write, think about exactly which adjective you want.
Choose an adjective which describes something clearly.

Example:

The adjective great can mean many different things.

What exactly do you want it to mean? It is not clear enough.

It was a great film. (exciting? frightening? well-acted? funny? sad?)

They have a great house. (huge? old? new? in the country?)

I bought a great pair of shoes. (fashionable? comfortable? high? cheap?)

Think of adjectives which are colours.

Put them in the correct section of the rainbow.

Here are some ideas for you.

You can write these in, too.

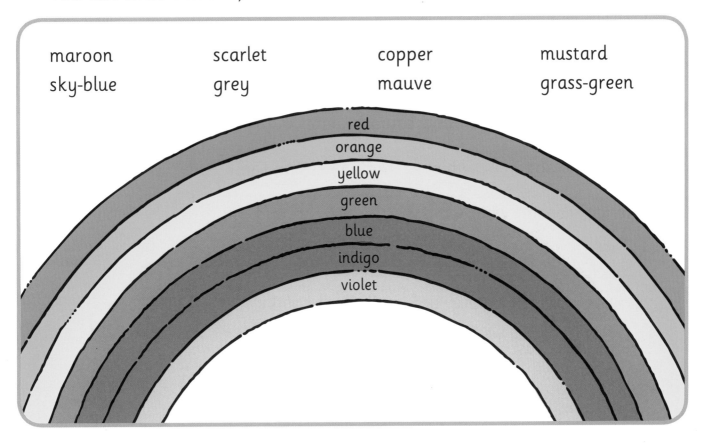

maroon   scarlet   copper   mustard
sky-blue   grey   mauve   grass-green

red
orange
yellow
green
blue
indigo
violet

Adjectives – choosing for meaning

Different adjectives change the feeling of a sentence. You are the writer, so you can make your reader feel what you want.

Example:

The cat's fur was soft and smooth between my fingers.

The cat's fur was bristly and tangled between my fingers.

You can see that the writer was trying to show a different feeling in each.

In the first one, the writer liked stroking the cat's healthy, clean fur.

In the second one, the writer did not like stroking the cat, as the fur was horrible.

Maybe the second cat was a stray or was ill.

Read each pair of sentences. Which sentences give a good feeling and which give a bad or nasty feeling?

	Feeling
1. The stones were cold and painful under my feet.	good/bad
2. The stones were warm and smooth under my feet.	good/bad
3. The gentle soft wind whipped the hair around my face.	good/bad
4. The icy piercing wind whipped the hair around my face.	good/bad
5. My bedroom felt calm, peaceful and quiet.	good/bad
6. My bedroom felt empty, unfriendly and creaky.	good/bad
7. The cheese crust was brown and tough.	good/bad
8. The cheese crust was golden and crispy.	good/bad

Adjectives and verbs can change the meaning and feeling of a whole story. Use them carefully in your own writing. Writing which describes details is called **descriptive writing**.

Example:
Here is some descriptive writing.
Notice the words underlined.

The <u>foul</u> monster <u>lurched</u> towards me with its <u>dripping</u> jaws open and its <u>hot</u> breath <u>stinking</u> of <u>rotten</u> eggs.

I could have used other words but these were the ones I wanted.
Does it sound frightening?
Would you have chosen other words?

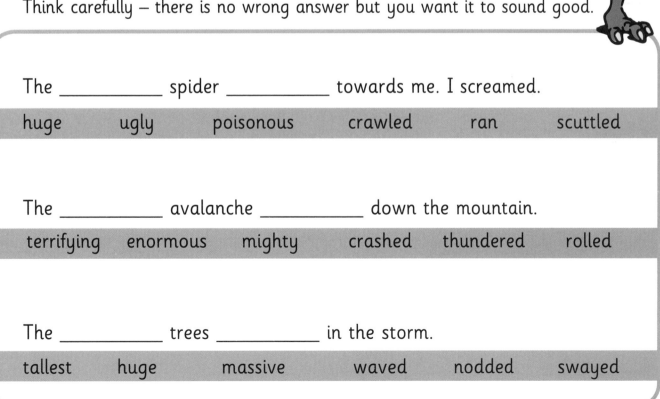

Choose the best verb or adjective from each list.

Think carefully – there is no wrong answer but you want it to sound good.

The _____ spider _____ towards me. I screamed.

| huge | ugly | poisonous | crawled | ran | scuttled |

The _____ avalanche _____ down the mountain.

| terrifying | enormous | mighty | crashed | thundered | rolled |

The _____ trees _____ in the storm.

| tallest | huge | massive | waved | nodded | swayed |

When we compare things, we use adjectives that talk about more, less, most and least.

Comparative – when an adjective describes something as being **more** or **less** than something else, we say it is a comparative adjective.

Examples: bigger, smaller, happier, darker (and irregular ones, e.g. better)

Superlative – when an adjective describes something as being the **most** or **least**, we say it is a *superlative adjective*.

Examples: biggest, smallest, happiest, darkest (and irregular ones, e.g. best)

Fill in this chart. The first one has been done for you.

Top tip:
Be careful with *good* and *bad*. They are both irregular adjectives!

Adjective	Comparative adjective	Superlative adjective
sad	sadder	saddest
quick		
brave		
thin		
large		
fast		
good		
bad		

Adjectives - comparing things

Most comparatives and superlatives end in **-er** and **-est**.
But some have a different rule: we don't change the ending but we put the words more or most before the adjective.
The adjectives that do this usually have more than two syllables.
All adjectives which end in **-ful** also do this.

Examples: beautiful   more beautiful   most beautiful

usual   more usual   most usual

hopeful   more hopeful   most hopeful

Important: If comparing only two things, always use the comparative, not the superlative. **Example:** This is the larger of the two dogs.

Put the correct comparative or superlative of each word in brackets.

1. She is the _____ (skilful) player on the team.

2. It was _____ (painful) than I imagined.

3. It was the _____ (terrible) day of the whole summer.

4. That was the _____ (horrifying) story I've ever read.

5. Jill is the _____ (intelligent) of my two sisters.

6. I am _____ (experienced) than everyone in my class.

7. He was the _____ (brilliant) boxer the world has known.

8. I looked even _____ (ridiculous) than a clown.

You know about comparatives and superlatives. Another way to compare and describe is to choose adjectives which show different degrees of something.

Example: Think of the words *hot* and *warm*. *Hot* is hotter than *warm*. But there are many other adjectives which describe different degrees of heat.

Here are some more: boiling, lukewarm, tepid, room temperature. *Boiling* is the hottest and *tepid* is the least hot.

Here are some groups of three adjectives. In each, write the words on a scale, starting with the most intense and ending with the least intense.

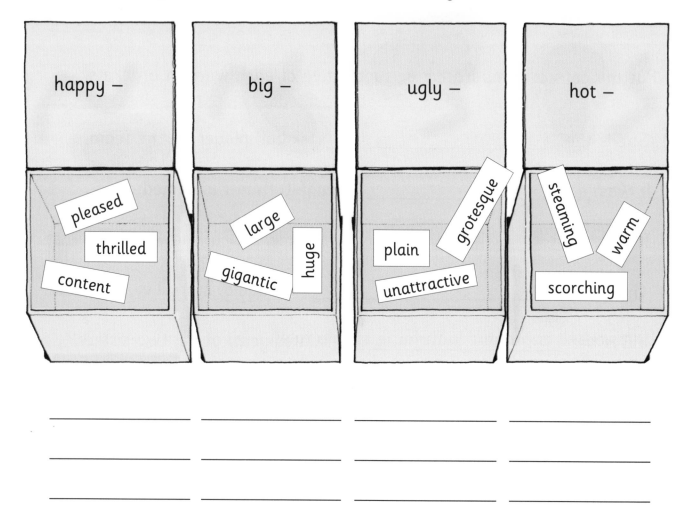

happy –   big –   ugly –   hot –

pleased   thrilled   content

large   gigantic   huge

plain   grotesque   unattractive

steaming   warm   scorching

_____   _____   _____   _____

_____   _____   _____   _____

_____   _____   _____   _____

You know about adjectives now. But sometimes an adjective is part of a group of words which stick together to do the describing work. We say that a group of words like this is called an **adjectival phrase**. In other words, it's a **phrase** which is doing the job of an **adjective**.

Example:

a (wrinkled) face ⟵——————— adjective

a face (with deep wrinkles around the eyes) ⟵——— adjectival phrase

Her face was (deeply wrinkled around the eyes.) ⟵——— adjectival phrase

All the words go together and describe the face.

Underline an adjectival phrase in each sentence. The first is done for you.

1. The moon, <u>perfectly round and clear</u>, shone brightly.

2. I bought a skirt with black spots.

3. The film was much too frightening.

4. My house is very expensively decorated.

5. I like books with plenty of excitement.

6. Football is a game with fairly simple rules.

7. The house was too small for our family.

8. The car was the smallest imaginable.

9. My first car was red with a green stripe down the middle.

10. A furry animal, all covered in leaves and mud, stared up at him.

We need punctuation so that our writing makes sense and is easy to read.
The most important punctuation mark is the full stop.
Every sentence has a full stop at the end and a capital letter at the start.
A question needs a question mark at the end, doesn't it?
And something that is loud or funny could have an exclamation mark!

Example:

I have a cherry tree in my garden. It is about five years old.
The cherries come in August. Do you like cherries?

Full stops help to make your writing clearer.

Put the full stops, question marks and capital
letters in the right places:

we went to greece last july   it was as hot as a desert   have you ever been

we stayed in a house on a mountain   what do you think was the best thing

about the house   it was the swimming pool   it was so blue and beautifully

refreshing after a hot day at the beach   we liked the greek food

the tomatoes were the biggest I have ever seen

Commas separate things in a list.
Commas also separate parts of sentences.
When a sentence has a main part (which would make sense on its own) and you add another part before or after it, you need a comma to separate the parts.

Example:

(added bit)   (main bit)
<u>When we arrived,</u>   <u>there was no one there.</u>

(main bit)   (added bit)
<u>She likes cabbage,</u>   <u>which is very unusual.</u>

Put in the capital letters, commas and full stops.
Underline the main part (the part that could make sense on its own).

1.   i took her to the doctor   who said she would be fine

2.   with a huge leap   the kangaroo jumped out of its cage

3.   if i had a million pounds   i would love to go round the world

4.   rome is the capital of italy   which is in europe

5.   i prefer the red one   even though it is quite old

You already know some of the uses of commas: to separate items on a list, or to separate parts of a sentence. There are special names for these parts of a sentence. Every sentence has a **main clause** – that's the bit which makes sense on its own. Many sentences also have another **phrase**, which would not make sense on its own.

This makes sense

Examples: I love apples, especially when they are sweet and juicy.

When they are sweet and juicy, apples are my favourite fruit.

so does this. That means it's the main clause

In these sentences, underline the main clause (the bit that makes sense on its own).

1. I don't want to go, if you're not.

2. She ran down the street, dragging her shopping behind her.

3. With a deafening crash, the great tree fell to the ground.

4. Hoping for a bone, the dog sat outside the butcher's shop.

5. I looked carefully at his face, waiting for some sign of recognition.

6. Without her help, I could never have managed it.

7. Shielding our eyes from the heat, we roasted chestnuts on the bonfire.

8. Blushing a deep purple colour, she managed to recite her poem.

The phrase which does not make sense on its own is called **subordinate** or **dependent**. Sometimes the subordinate phrase is in the middle of a sentence, breaking the main part of the sentence in half. When this happens, the subordinate phrase needs a comma before and after it.

Examples:

The man, not looking where he was going, tripped over a stick.

The man tripped over a stick is the main clause because it is the part which makes sense on its own.

not looking where he was going is extra, so it has a comma on each side.

Each of these sentences is like that. Put a comma on each side of the subordinate, or extra, part.

1. The man clutching his bag tightly shouted at the thieves.

2. A tree swaying violently in the wind suddenly fell onto the road.

3. An enormous creature covered in mud and dripping with water appeared out of the mist.

4. Millions of people even quite old ones are learning to use computers.

5. My last thought just before I fell asleep was how much I was dreading tomorrow.

Look how important it is to put commas in the correct places.
Can you see the *very* different meanings of these two sentences?

That man said the boy stole the money.　　Who stole it? _____

That man, said the boy, stole the money.　　Who stole it? _____

Semicolons and colons

Semicolons **;** are very useful. They are stronger than commas but less strong than full stops. There are two places to use them.

a) **instead of a full stop**, when a sentence seems linked to the one before. Many people wrongly use a comma because they think a sentence hasn't finished. If you feel that the meaning carries on, use a semicolon.

Example: I went to London last week; we had a wonderful time.
(A full stop would have been fine; a comma would have been wrong.)

b) **instead of a comma**, to separate items in a list when each item is long.

Example: My favourite activities are riding a bike in the rain, especially if it's muddy; visiting my friends in the country; and collecting fossils from the caves on our beach.

All the punctuation is missing in these sentences. Can you put commas, semicolons and full stops in all the right places?

Top tip:
Don't put a capital letter after a semicolon – except *I*.

1. I want to be an athlete   I'm going to go on a special course

   in the summer

2. The sun shone through a milky haze   it was still too cold for me

3. Straining my eyes in the fog I could just see the hut   I wondered if we could

   reach it before darkness

4. I liked the one with pink ears   the one which had a patch on its eye   both the

   ones with black spots and whiskers   and the one with the fluffiest tail

5. I want you to investigate how the people in the rainforest live   what their houses

   are like   what they eat   what they wear   what sorts of technology they have

   and what medicines they use

A colon $:$ is a special way of linking two parts of a sentence.
The rules about them are simple. You can easily improve your writing by using colons in the right places.

When to use a colon:
a) to introduce a list
(Did you see how I used one at the beginning of this list about using colons?)

b) when you are about to explain what you have just said
Example: I hate fish: it makes me feel sick.
Here, the colon means because: I hate fish because it makes me feel sick.

In these sentences, put either a colon or a semicolon in the box.
Put a colon if you think the meaning is because. If not, put a semicolon.
In fact, it would not really be wrong to put a semicolon in all these places,
but try to judge the exact meaning so that you use the better one.

1. I was quite amazed ☐ there was money all over the path.

2. The sun was blazing down ☐ there wasn't a cloud to be seen.

3. I want to be an astronaut ☐ I think it would be very exciting.

4. I decided I would go ☐ it would be better than staying indoors.

5. The mist swirled around our feet ☐ it made everything seem eerie.

6. I gasped in horror ☐ there was a face at the window. It grinned at me.

7. Most plants grow better in warm places ☐ the sun helps them grow.

A contraction is when we squash two words together and miss out one or more letters.
We use an apostrophe to show where the letters are missing.

Examples:

n't = not	can**'t**, must**n't**, should**n't**, could**n't**, would**n't**, did**n't**, do**n't**, does**n't**, wo**n't** (will not), has**n't**, had**n't**
'll = will	he**'ll**, she**'ll**, they**'ll**, I**'ll**, you**'ll**, we**'ll**
've = have	you**'ve**, they**'ve**, I**'ve**, we**'ve**
'd = would or had	I**'d**, she**'d**, you**'d**, he**'d**, they**'d**, we**'d**
're = are	you**'re**, they**'re**, we**'re**
's = is or has	he**'s**, it**'s**, she**'s**, that**'s**

Make contractions for the underlined words:

1. I think <u>I will</u> go for a walk now. _____

2. We <u>should have</u> listened harder. _____

3. <u>She is</u> the best tennis player <u>I have</u> ever seen. _____ _____

4. <u>We are</u> going to New York for Christmas. _____

5. <u>That is</u> something I <u>had not</u> thought about. _____ _____

6. You <u>should not</u> wear your best clothes in the mud. _____

7. Be careful or <u>you will</u> break something. _____

8. I <u>will not</u> watch what <u>you are</u> doing. _____ _____

There are two things to be careful about with contractions.
First, make sure the apostrophe goes exactly where the missing letters are.
Second, be careful with words that **sound** or **look like** contractions.

Examples:

We're going to get a new cat. (Stands for *we are*.)
We were in the garden when it began to snow. (Doesn't stand for *we are*.)

It's freezing today. (Stands for *it is*.)
The cat ate its food. (Doesn't stand for *it is*.)

We'll help. (Stands for *we will*.)
The wheel broke. (Doesn't stand for *we will*!)

If you always think about the meaning, it will be easy.

Write a conversation between two friends, using as many contractions as you can. Write their names in the boxes:

Apostrophes for possession

Apostrophes tell us about **possession**, or who owns something.

There are two important things to think about:

a) Do I need one?

A word ending in s only needs an apostrophe if the next word (or words) belong to it.

The apostrophe stands for of.

Example: *the girl's bike* – the bike of the girl

the boy's very expensive pen – the very expensive pen of the boy

the man's manners – the manners of the man

b) Where do I put it?

Immediately after the owner or owners.

Example: *the dog's tail was wagging* – the tail of the dog (one dog)

the dogs' tails were wagging – the tails of the dogs (several dogs)

Rewrite each phrase with an apostrophe in the correct place:

1. my mums car

_____

2. Sarahs house

_____

3. the teachers mistake

_____

4. the horses tails

_____

5. ladies shoes

_____

6. todays news

_____

7. this drivers fault

_____

8. a doctors coat

_____

9. the cats tails

_____

10. my bikes brakes

_____

11. my dads office

_____

12. my friends hair

_____

Which of these do not need an apostrophe?

Apples are healthy. ☐   I like sausages best. ☐   A girls face ☐

There are no exceptions to the rules about apostrophes for possession. **But** there are a few things to be careful about. If you remember to put the apostrophe immediately after the owner or owners, you will be fine.

Look out for:

a) words which end in **s** even when they are not plural:

Example: Charles' car – Charles ends in s.

You can put another **s** on (Charles's car) if you want to.

b) plurals which do not end in **s**:

Example: the children's party – children is plural and it is the party **of the children**, so the apostrophe goes after children.

c) when we can see that a word is missed out:

Example: I like my hat but not Sally's – we know that it means Sally's hat.

Example: I'm going round to Gran's – meaning Gran's house.

Write each phrase or sentence with the apostrophes in the correct places. Be careful with the last one!

Top tip:
Only the *owner* needs an apostrophe.

1. the mens room
_____

2. James job
_____

3. a childrens entertainer
_____

4. womens clothes
_____

5. Mrs Jones car
_____

6. a babys pram
_____

7. I left Sarahs at 4 o'clock
_____

8. Isn't that car your mums?
_____

9. Helens is a very strange hairstyle
_____

10. their wives jobs
_____

11. The colours of Josephs coat were extraordinary
_____

You have almost learnt everything about apostrophes now.
There are just two more important but simple rules:

a) these words never have an apostrophe: hers, theirs, ours, yours
b) **it's** only has an apostrophe for abbreviation.

It is ...

Does not mean _it is_
or _it has_

Example: It's funny that the dog hasn't eaten its dinner.

Write each sentence with apostrophes in the correct places.
Be careful – some sentences don't need any.

1. Jims car is much smarter than ours.

2. Theirs is much more comfortable than his.

3. A lorry has shed its load in the middle of our road.

4. Its quite astonishing how much food he can eat.

5. Have you seen how hard its snowing?

6. The tree lost most of its branches in the storm.

7. The man said he was a friend of ours.

8. An old woman with bright eyes came right over to where the boys sat.

Let's see how much you can remember. Here are the rules again:

- a word needs an apostrophe if:
  - one or more letters are missed out (abbreviation)
  - the word (or words) after it belong to it (possession)
- the apostrophe for **abbreviation** goes **where the letters are missing**
- the apostrophe for **possession** goes **immediately after the owner**
- ours, yours, hers and theirs never have apostrophes
- it's has an apostrophe only if it stands for it is or it has

Now look carefully at these sentences.

Write each one with apostrophes where necessary.

Beware: there are two sentences which don't need an apostrophe at all.

1. I ran gasping to my uncles house.

2. Theres a terrible monster who lives in that cave.

3. The Vikings ships invaded Britain a thousand years ago.

4. The ancient Greeks worshipped many different gods.

5. James brother was our schools best runner.

6. We often go round to Mrs Blacks for a meal.

7. My sisters like pizza but I prefer Chinese meals.

8. Childrens meals should be full of energy and goodness.

9. The mens quiz team came equal with the womens.

10. The submarines sharp grey noses reared from the water like sharks fins.

We add a **prefix** to the **beginning** of a word to change its meaning. You can use prefixes to make lots of new words. This will improve your writing and help you to understand longer words that you read.

Example:
submarine = under the sea
subterranean = under the ground
subsoil = under the soil

so the prefix **sub** means **under**

Circle the prefix. Use a dictionary to work out what each prefix means:

circumference, circumnavigate   _____

biannual, biped, bicentenary   _____

prefix, prefer, predict   _____

expel, export, exclude   _____

polysyllabic, polymath, polygon   _____

These prefixes make a word mean **not** something: *un il ir dis mis im in*
Guess the meanings of these words:

disagree   _____   irregular   _____

impolite   _____   misunderstand   _____

We add a **suffix** to the **end** of a word. Sometimes it changes the meaning. Usually it gives the word a different use in a sentence.

Example:

The suffix **er** is very common.

Look what happens when we add it to a verb:
hunt + **er** = hunter (someone who hunts)

Look what happens when we add it to an adjective:
cold + **er** = colder (more cold)

Here are some suffixes: less   ful   ly   er   ess   ous   ness
Add the correct one to these words:

1. A scarf is use_____ in very hot weather. (Be careful here!)

2. I used to have a love_____ coat with eight pockets.

3. I have never met a fam_____ person.

4. I am quite hope_____ that it will be sunny tomorrow.

5. A lion_____ is a female lion.

6. My brother is a wait_____ in a smart restaurant.

7. The host_____ provided a wonder_____ meal.

8. The cold_____ made her teeth rattle.

Definitions of words

Explaining what a word means is called **defining** or **giving a definition**.
You must try to give the most exact definition you can.
Imagine you are talking to someone who doesn't understand.

You can't use the word in your definition.
So you can't say, '*Gobble means gobble food.*'

Example:

gobble = eat greedily or fast
If you just said eat, this would not show the
special meaning of *gobble*.

Give an exact definition of these words:

carpet _____

whisper _____

pencil _____

saucepan _____

climb _____

hop _____

slower _____

Sometimes a word has several meanings. Choose the meaning which makes sense in the sentence that you are reading.

Example:

I can't bear cheese

bear = put up with (not a wild animal!)

Read the story of the Pied Piper.
Write definitions for the underlined words:

Many years ago, in the German town of Hamelin, the people had a <u>terrible</u> problem with rats. There were rats everywhere – in the streets, houses, flower <u>beds</u>, even in babies' cots. The mayor did not know what to do. One day, a <u>peculiar</u> man called the Pied Piper arrived and said he could <u>deal</u> with the problem if the mayor would pay a huge <u>sum</u> of money. The mayor <u>agreed</u>.

The Pied Piper played his pipes and the rats followed him out of Hamelin and fell over a cliff. 'I <u>refuse</u> to pay!' said the mayor. So the Pied Piper played his pipes again. This time every child followed the Piper. They never <u>returned</u>.
The mayor had learnt his lesson, but much too late.

terrible	_____	sum	_____
beds	_____	agreed	_____
peculiar	_____	refuse	_____
deal	_____	returned	_____

More definitions

Your definitions must match the word. So if the word is plural, or a past tense, or if a verb ends in -**ing**, your definition must be the same.

Example:
jump – leap high in the air
jumping – leaping high in the air
jumped – leapt high in the air

Write definitions of these words. You can test your skill by reading your definition to a friend and seeing if he or she can guess the word.

a football _____

joking _____

magazines _____

swim _____

swam _____

largest _____

homes _____

Here are some definitions. What do you think they are?

1. A small building for keeping garden tools in. _____

2. Something you use to erase pencil marks. _____

3. Yellow creamy sauce, hot or cold, for puddings. _____

When we define a word, we have to notice whether it is a noun, a verb, an adjective or whatever. The definition must match this.

Example:

is dancing — (present tense verb) moving in time to the music
a dance — (singular noun) a way of moving in time to music
dancers — (plural noun) people who can move in time to music
danced — (past tense verb) moved in time to music

Now write short definitions of these words. Pay attention to the ending and form of the word and make sure your definitions match.

Top tip:
One way to define a word is to say its opposite: you could say that *tallest* means the opposite of *shortest*.

1. champions _____

2. widest _____

3. gardening _____

4. flew _____

5. keyboards _____

6. dictionary _____

7. chattering _____

8. swallowed _____

Alphabetical order

Now that you know about nouns, verbs and adjectives, you can find lots of them in books that you read. If you read different stories, you will find many ideas for words that you can use in your own writing. You could make your own dictionary by writing words in order.

Example:

Make an alphabetical list of the adjectives in this passage.

The <u>ancient</u> Greeks believed in gods	**a**ncient
who were often <u>violent</u> or <u>cruel</u>.	**c**ruel
They often gave <u>terrible</u> punishments to people	**t**errible
who annoyed them.	**v**iolent

Underline the nine adjectives in this story and put them in an alphabetical list:

Echo was a beautiful Greek girl. The king of the

gods, Zeus, liked her and bought her a present.

Zeus' jealous wife, Hera, was furious. She gave

Echo an awful punishment: first, she made her

invisible. Then she made a cruel rule that Echo

could only repeat what people said. After that,

Echo had a miserable and lonely life because

no one knew she was there and she could never

say what she wanted to say.

_____

_____

_____

_____

_____

_____

_____

_____

_____

Sometimes you will read a word that you don't know. Think about how it makes sense in a sentence. You may need to look the word up in a dictionary. To help you remember the word so you can use it yourself, add it to your own dictionary. Dictionaries always use alphabetical order. If two words start with the same letter, look at the second letters. If they are the same, look at the third.

Example:
These verbs start with **d**. To put them in the right order, we look at the second letters. Then the third letters.

dragged   drinking   dawdled   1. d<u>a</u>wdled   2. dr<u>a</u>gged   3. dr<u>i</u>nking

Put the underlined verbs in this Aesop's fable into alphabetical order. Look up any meanings that you don't know:

A dog <u>darted</u> into a stable and <u>leapt</u> into a

manger full of hay. The horse <u>complained</u>, 'Hey,

you! <u>Disappear</u>! You don't even like hay!'

'So what? I don't <u>care</u>,' <u>responded</u> the dog.

'I just <u>adore</u> making life difficult for you.'

When someone <u>acts</u> like this, we call them

'dog in the manger'.

1 _____

2 _____

3 _____

4 _____

5 _____

6 _____

7 _____

8 _____

Below are some interesting words, many of which you probably don't know. Pick five that you would like to know. Put them in alphabetical order. Then use a dictionary to find what they mean – you will need an adult dictionary.

Which is your favourite word? Do you like it because of the sound or the meaning? Now that you know so many interesting words, see if you can use one or two next time you write a story. Your teacher will be impressed!

Top tip:
Have you found any other words you like? You can find some very weird words when you browse through a big dictionary!

My five chosen words are:

_____   _____   _____   _____   _____

polka

plumage   1. _____   =   _____

pollywog   2. _____   =   _____

pluvial

pointillism   3. _____   =   _____

polyp

pockmarked   4. _____   =   _____

plummet

pomp   5. _____   =   _____

plink

You have now nearly finished this section. Here's a fun exercise to do before you move on to Reading Comprehension.

Ask your friend or a grown-up to say a noun. How many adjectives can you think of that might describe the noun, beginning with these letters?

Write your noun here

m _____

n _____

o _____

p _____

a _____   q _____

b _____   r _____

c _____   s _____

d _____   t _____

e _____   u _____

f _____   v _____

g _____   w _____

h _____

Score:
1 point for a 2-letter word
2 points for a 3-letter word
3 points for a 4-letter word
4 points for a 5-letter word

i _____

j _____

Write your score here

k _____

l _____

A story is something that a writer makes up. There might be some true things in it, but it's really just for fun and not meant to be true. This is called fiction. There are different types of story: adventure, ghost, fairy, love stories; traditional stories, fables, myths. How can you tell what sort of story it is? And how can you tell it's fiction and not an information book?

- You can look at the title, the cover and what's inside.
- The picture on the front may have clues about the type of story.
- If it's a story, there won't be an index at the back.
- There may be a list of chapter headings near the front – the chapter headings will tell you if it's a story or an information book.
- On the back cover you will find more clues about what the book is about.

Get the story book you are reading or one you have read before.
Answer these questions.

Title: _____ Author: _____

What is on the cover? Is the picture funny/frightening/ordinary?

_____

What is Chapter 1 called? _____

Is there an index at the back? _____

Would you use this book to find out about things for a school project?

_____

What is the book about? (Does the back cover tell you?) _____

_____

You could read poems, as well. Poems are usually fiction.
They can tell stories or they can describe something in a special way. They can make you feel something strongly or they can be funny.

Read this poem:

There was an old man of Peru,
Who dreamed he was eating his shoe.
He woke in the night,
In a terrible fright,
And found it was perfectly true!

If this was not a poem, it could be written like this:
Once there was an old man who lived in Peru, which is a country in South America. One night he dreamed that he was eating his shoe. Suddenly he woke up in a terrible panic – goodness me! – he really was eating his shoe!

1. How do they look different? _____

_____

2. What is special about the last word in each line of the poem?

_____

3. Which has more words – the poem or the story? _____

4. As you read the poem, drum the words with your hand.

   Do the same with the story. What is the difference? _____

_____

_____

A **play** is another type of fiction. This is when some people act out a story. The person who writes a play is called a **playwright**. A playwright writes the words for the actors to say. The playwright also writes what the actors should do: this is called a **stage direction**.

Here is a bit from a play. (*Stage directions are written like this and in brackets.*)

(*A man and a woman are sitting in a restaurant.*)

Mr Jones:	Well, Helen, I must say – this is quite ridiculous. We've been waiting at least 10 minutes and no one's taken our order yet.
Mrs Jones:	Oh, I'm sure it's only 5 minutes, dear. We must be patient. Everyone is terribly busy.
Mr Jones:	Well it's just not good enough. (He shouts very loudly.) Waiter!
Man with a tray:	(Coming over very slowly and looking cross.) Sir?
Mr Jones:	This is ridiculous, young man. Why can't someone take our order?
Man with a tray:	Because, sir, this is a self-service restaurant.

1. How many people are in this part of the play? _____

2. Where does the play take place? _____

3. Underline the stage directions.

4. How many times does Mrs Jones speak? _____

5. Write what you think Mr Jones or Mrs Jones would say and do next. Mr Jones might be embarrassed or carry on being cross – you decide.

_____

_____

_____

There are lots of different sorts of information books, too. These are called non-fiction. If you are trying to find out something, you need to learn how to find the right book. You need a book that's right for your age, too, or the information won't help you.

Here are some things you might want to find out. Draw a line to match them to the best book. For some, you might use **two** books.

A. the meaning of a word

B. things about deserts

C. what people ate in Roman times

D. the inventor of television

E. how to spell 'envelope'

F. how volcanoes happen

1. What is the difference between an encyclopedia and a book about dinosaurs? _____

2. Look up dinosaur in a dictionary and then in an encyclopedia.

   Which tells you more? _____

3. Does that book tell you enough for a project or would you need to find another book, too? _____

A writer writes what he wants to say. (Of course, writers can be 'he' or 'she', but let's say 'he' for now.)

He might write true information: bits of true information are called **facts**.

He might want to make up a story: we call this **fiction**.

Or he might write what he believes: this is called **opinion**.

He may do a mixture: a made-up story might contain some facts as well.

When you read, you need to know whether you are reading fact, fiction or opinion.
A magazine often contains all these.

Look at this list of contents and tick the most appropriate column.

Page		fact	fiction	opinion
1	Editor's comment			
2	Letters – you say what you feel			
3	Caring for your pet			
5	The Dark Forest – a story from Finland			
8	Bullying in Schools – we investigate the truth			
11	Should Smoking be Banned?			
14	How our Laws are Made			
19	Love Your Neighbour – the final part of our moving tale			
24	You Speak Out – a reader gives her views			

Top tip:
Have a look at a real magazine's contents: can you work out which features will be fact, fiction and opinion?

Sometimes, a writer will try to make you think he is writing facts, when really it is just opinion. You need to think carefully and decide whether you are reading something that is true or not.

Some writing tries to persuade you to think a particular way: you can choose to think that way or you can decide whether you have a different opinion yourself.

Here is a passage about smoking:

Smoking often causes serious illness. It sometimes kills. Everyone who smokes will die from it. Passive smoking means breathing in the smoke from other people's cigarettes. The Government must ban smoking in public places. Some restaurants already ban smoking. Many public places, such as trains and buses also have rules about smoking. The only place where people should be allowed to smoke is in their own homes.

1. Underline the statements that are definitely facts.

2. Circle the one that is meant to sound like a fact, but is untrue.

3. Why has the writer included it? _____

4. Underline in blue the statements that are opinions.

5. Would everyone agree with this passage? _____

Which of these are facts? Put a tick:

If today is Monday, tomorrow is Tuesday.   _____

Chocolate is nicer than strawberry.   _____

Mount Everest is the most wonderful place in the world.   _____

There are 100 centimetres in a metre.   _____

Top tip:
Remember:
it's wrong to write or say something untrue, just to make your argument stronger.

A fiction writer has to think about lots of things to make a good story. Read the story that starts on this page. When you've answered the questions on the next page, you will find that the story carries on.

WHY THE SEA IS SALTY

Once upon a time, many hundreds of years ago, a poor man called Hans was trudging home through the huge dark forest with trees as tall as houses. It was nearly night. There was thick snow, and wind rattled the branches. Hans' feet were cold in his thin shoes but it was nearly Christmas and he was carrying a wonderful ham which his rich brother had given him.

The rich brother was mean and greedy. He wore the most expensive clothes, ate the most expensive food and slept in the most expensive sheets that anyone had ever seen. He only ever gave Hans a present once a year.

Deep in the thickest, darkest, coldest, deepest part of the forest, just when his feet were so cold and tired that he thought they might drop off, Hans met an old man with a long white beard. There was something most odd about the man. He seemed to appear from nowhere. Also his shoes were thin but he did not seem to notice the cold.

When we read a story, we need to know some things as soon as possible. We want to know **where** and **when** the story is happening: this is called the **setting**. So the writer has to give us some details to tell us where and when.

The writer also has to make the reader feel the **atmosphere**. This means things like: is it mysterious? cold? frightening? funny? strange or ordinary?

Read the previous page again.

1. Where is this part of the story set?

   _____

2. What is this place like? Can you find three details that tell us how the place looked?

   _____

3. When does the story happen? Circle all the things which are true.

   a long time ago   a couple of years ago   yesterday

   in the spring   January   before Christmas

   in the middle of the night   evening

4. What is the atmosphere like so far? Tick the things you agree with.

A. The writer wants me to feel that it's very cold, dark and spooky.   ☐

B. Hans has a happy life and doesn't have to work too hard.   ☐

C. The old man is mysterious and will turn out to be special in some way.   ☐

D. It's an everyday story of things that could happen to all of us.   ☐

Dialogue

Here, the story about Hans continues. It has been written like a play.

Old man: Good evening, sir. What a wonderful ham that is!

Hans: It's a present from my rich brother.

Old man: If your brother is so rich, why are you so poor?

Hans: (*looking sad*) Well, I suppose because my brother is not at all kind. He and his wife are so greedy you would hardly believe it.

Old man: Listen, sir. I like to help people who are poor and good, like you. Take the ham to the dwarves who live below this tree. But don't sell it for money – tell them you want the old salt-grinder that they keep near their fire.

Hans: But I don't want an old salt-grinder! Why on earth would I?

Old man: (*smiling kindly*) Trust me, sir. I'll tell you when you come back.

(*Hans goes under the tree. While he is gone, the old man does cartwheels and handstands and pulls four rabbits out of a hat.*)

Hans: (*returning with a scruffy salt-grinder*) So? What now?

Old man: Just ask it for anything you want. But to stop it, say, 'Grind not, my mill,' three times. Happy Christmas, Hans! (*He vanishes.*)

Dialogue

In a story, the characters often speak. When this happens we call it **dialogue**.
A story-writer uses speech marks round the words that are spoken.
On page 52 you saw how a playwright writes conversation. Do you remember about
stage directions? Look at page 52 if you can't remember.

1. How many stage directions are there in the dialogue on the previous page?

_____

2. What does this page tell you about the old man?
   (Look at the stage directions <u>and</u> what he says.)

_____

_____

3. Can you imagine what Hans and the dwarves said to each other?
   (Put in any stage directions you need.)

Hans: _____

Dwarf: _____

_____

Hans: _____

Dwarf: _____

_____

Hans: _____

Dwarf: _____

_____

Now the story continues.

Hans ran back home, very excited to find out what the salt-grinder could do. For years, he and his wife had been very poor. They worked hard and always did their best but it was difficult to make ends meet.

As soon as he got home, he gave his wife a kiss and proudly put the grinder on the table. His wife looked rather puzzled. 'A salt-grinder,' she said. 'How lovely, dear!' She was a kind woman who never complained about anything.

Hans couldn't wait any longer. He said loudly, 'Now, little salt-grinder, grind me a delicious supper!' And immediately the table was covered with the most wonderful food: a roast chicken, golden potatoes, rich thick gravy and delicious tiny peas. His wife gasped in delight.

That Christmas was the best they had ever had. Everything they asked the grinder for would suddenly appear: a beautiful tree hanging with silver bells, a huge turkey big enough for twenty people, and presents for all their friends.

Everyone saw that Hans and his wife were no longer poor. Hans was kind and gave people everything they needed. Life was good in that little village.

Hans' brother heard about this salt-grinder. He was a mean, jealous and greedy man. Although he was rich, he wanted even more.

The people or animals in a story are the characters.
A writer needs to show us exactly what the characters are like.
A character could be good or bad, mean or kind, grumpy or happy, young
or old. And there may be special details about the character: perhaps someone
hates dogs, or someone is very rich.
We must notice how they speak and what they do.

From the story so far, can you answer these questions?

1. Tick which one of these is true about Hans:

A. He is very frightened of the dark.

B. He works very hard but does not earn much money.

C. He is mean to his wife.

2. Which of these is true about Hans' wife?

A. She does not work very hard.

B. She often complains about her difficult life and how poor she is.

C. She loves Hans and is happy with him, even though they are poor.

3. Write three things about Hans' brother.

_____

_____

_____

4. When his wife said 'How lovely, dear!' what does that tell us about her?

_____

Here is the last part of the story.

The greedy brother visited Hans. Hans gave him a wonderful meal and his wife said he must stay as long as he wanted. But Hans' brother was not there for a friendly visit. In the night, he stole the salt-grinder and left.

The brother went to his ship and sailed out to sea. He had a plan to become even richer. Salt was very valuable in those days and he planned to tell the grinder to grind enough salt to fill fifty thousand sacks. Then he could sell the salt and be the richest man in the world.

'Now, little salt-grinder, grind me some salt!' he shouted. And sure enough the grinder began to grind. Soon all fifty thousand sacks were full.

'Stop grinding now!' shouted the brother. But the grinder did not stop. He shouted again, 'Stop! You stupid grinder!' But these were the wrong words.

The grinder carried on and on. Soon there was so much salt that the ship sank and the greedy brother drowned. Still the grinder carried on grinding salt and it is still grinding today. And that is why the sea is salty.

How a story ends is very important. It often tells us the point of the story.
It could be happy, sad, funny, or surprising.
Or it could teach us something.

Now that you have read the end of the story, you can answer the questions:

1. Who was punished for behaving badly? _____

2. Does this ending seem to teach us anything? _____

_____

3. Do you think it is right that Hans and his wife should have the magic

   salt-grinder? Say why you think this. _____

_____

_____

4. The story could have been different. Imagine that the brother does not steal the

   grinder. Which ending would you choose (or you can make one up)?

| Hans and his wife are happy and rich for the rest of their lives. | They start to become greedy and argue about everything, so they decide to throw the grinder away and go back to their simple life. | _____ _____ _____ _____ _____ |

5. Can you think of another story where a bad person is punished?

_____

There are many different sorts of poetry. Some poems have rhyming words. Some are funny or have a special pattern.
Other poems tell a story. Sometimes strange words are used and when we read a poem we have to use our imagination very well.

Here is part of a famous poem by Lewis Carroll, who also wrote
Alice in Wonderland. It is special because he has made up lots of the words.

'Twas brillig and the slithy toves
Did gyre and gimble in the wabe;
All mimsy were the borogoves,
And the mome raths outgrabe.

Beware the Jabberwock, my son!
The jaws that bite, the claws that catch!
Beware the Jubjub bird and shun
The frumious Bandersnatch!

And as in uffish thought he stood,
The Jabberwock, with eyes of flame,
Came whiffling through the tulgey wood
And burbled as it came.

One two! One two! and through and through
The vorpal blade went snicker-snack!
He left it dead and with its head
He went galumphing back.

Poetic language

1. Tick what you think the poem is about?

A. someone going for a walk in the woods ☐

B. someone killing a frightening dragon ☐

C. someone lighting a fire in a forest ☐

2. What can you say about this Jabberwocky creature?
   Tick three things that the poem tells us.

   it had eyes like fire ☐   it was blue ☐   it had four legs ☐

   it was dangerous ☐   it had wings ☐   it had claws ☐

3. The underlined words are made up by the poet.
   What could they mean?

   Came <u>whiffling</u> through the <u>tulgey</u> wood

   whiffling _____

   tulgey _____

4. Tick why you think the poet has made up words:

A. to confuse us ☐

B. because he's not good at thinking of real words ☐

C. to make the poem sound mysterious and strange ☐

5. Make up your own words to go in the spaces:

   Beware the _____ bird and shun

   The _____ Bandersnatch!

Some poems have a special pattern or **rhythm**. (Rhythm is like a musical beat.) A limerick is like this. It has five lines and the rhyming pattern is always the same. It is always funny – and usually very silly!

There was once an old lady of Riga
Who went out for a ride on a tiger.
They returned from the ride
With the lady inside,
And a smile on the face of the tiger.

1. What had happened to the lady? _____

The odd thing is that even though that might seem sad, it's still funny.

There is a special word to do with poetry. It is **scan**. To scan means to have the right number of beats in a line. If it doesn't scan, it sounds wrong.

There once was a man from Japan,
Whose poems never would scan,
When asked why it was,
He said, 'It's because
I always try to fit as many words into each line as I possibly can.'

2. Did the last line scan? _____

3. Was that on purpose? _____

Being a good writer is all about choosing the right word. You could choose a word because of how it **sounds**. Or what it **means**. Or both.

Here is a poem about the sea. It has two verses:

Yesterday the sea was sleeping,
Snoring softly in the sun.
While clear-blue waves were washing pebbles,
Playing tig and having fun.

Today the blackened sea is angry,
A fuming, furious, growling bear.
It lashes, crashes, smashes pebbles,
Spitting danger through the air.

1. In verse 1, find three words which make the sea seem like a living creature.

   _____

2. What colour was the sea in the verse 1? _____ Verse 2? _____

3. Copy out two lines where lots of the words begin with the same sound.

   _____

   _____

4. Find six words in verse 2 which make the sea sound rough.

   _____

5. Describe in your own words how the sea was on each day.

   _____

   _____

There are some more special words we use when we talk about poems. It's useful if you know what they mean, so that you can see how poems are put together.

verse: a section of a poem (rather like a paragraph)
stanza: another word for a verse
chorus: a verse which is repeated regularly throughout the poem or song
couplet: two lines which go together and rhyme
rhyme: when words have the same sound at the end
rhythm: the beat of a poem – you could clap in time to the rhythm

Read this poem by William Blake and answer the questions:

The sun descending in the west,
The evening star does shine;
The birds are silent in their nest,
And I must seek for mine.
The moon, like a flower
In heaven's high bower,
With silent delight
Sits and smiles on the night.

1. How many verses are there? _____

2. What is the first word of the last couplet? _____

3. Write the rhyming words of any lines which rhyme. _____

   _____

4. Is there a chorus? _____

5. Clap the rhythm with your hands. Is the second half of the poem the same rhythm as the first half? _____

6. Would you say that the rhythm is peaceful or exciting? _____

Some poems don't use rhyme. But ones that do have different patterns of rhyming lines. There's a special way we can describe how a poem rhymes.

Put **A** after the first line. If the next line rhymes with it, put **A** again.

As soon as you come to a line that doesn't rhyme with it, put **B**.

Continue, putting a new letter if a line doesn't rhyme with any that comes before.

Let's try. I've done the first one.

There was a young woman called Hollie,	**(A)**
Who wished that she was a collie.	**(A)**
The vet wouldn't help,	**(B)**
So she started to yelp,	**(B)**
But her husband just called her a wally.	**(A)**
Who has seen the wind?	( )
Neither I nor you;	( )
But when the leaves hang trembling	( )
The wind is passing through.	( )
Who has seen the wind?	( )
Neither you nor I;	( )
But when the trees bow down their heads	( )
The wind is passing by.	( )
(Christina Rossetti 1830–1894)	
A child should always say what's true,	( )
And speak when he is spoken to,	( )
And behave mannerly at table:	( )
At least as far as he is able.	( )
(R. L. Stevenson 1850–1894)	

Look at the poem on the previous page. Find the rhyming pattern.

_____

Which poem on this page consists completely of rhyming couplets?

_____

A dictionary tells you **meanings of words** and **spellings**.

Some dictionaries also tell you whether a word is a noun, verb etc. You need the right dictionary for your age.

Alphabetical order. Remember: if the first letter is the same, look at the second, then third. So *sag* comes before *sat*; and *sat* comes before *sauce*.

Here is part of a dictionary page: (n) means noun and (v) means verb

sauce   (n) something you put on food to make it tastier

shale   (n) tiny loose pieces of stone or grit

site   (n) a piece of land where something is built

source   (n) where something starts or comes from, such as a river

stare   (v) to look at something for a long time without blinking

Fill the spaces:

1. It is very rude to _____ (stare/stair).

2. A building _____ (sight/site) is a very dangerous place.

3. The tomato _____ (source/sauce) was finished.

Find the meanings of the underlined words:

4. The <u>shale</u> made the walk very difficult. _____

5. We walked to the <u>source</u> of the river. _____

Draw arrows to show where these words would go in the dictionary page above:

6. sprint   7. sense   8. surgeon

Information books are written so that you can easily find what you want.
Things might be in alphabetical order, like a dictionary or encyclopedia.
There might be a list of **contents** or chapter headings.
A history book might be in the order in which the events happened.

Here is a list of contents in a book about sharks:

	pages
Different types of shark	2 – 5
How dangerous are they?	6 – 10
Where they live	11 – 15
What they eat	16 – 19
All about baby sharks	20 – 24
Fascinating facts	25 – 28
Index	29 – 30

Write the page numbers where you would look for information about:

1. Food _____

2. Great white sharks _____

3. How sharks have babies _____

4. Whether they kill people _____

5. Places in the world where they live _____

6. What would you find on page 22? _____

When you look for information about something, you will find some things you want and some things you don't want.

To find what you want, do three things:

- think carefully about what you want
- look at chapter headings or the index
- then look at the first sentence of each paragraph

I wanted information about sharks. I found a book called Under the Sea and the index told me to look at page 9. You will find it on the next page.

Use it to answer these questions:

1. Put a circle round any paragraphs that are about sharks.

2. Name two sharks that are not dangerous to humans _____

   and _____.

3. What is plankton?_____

4. What are the first three words of the paragraph about great white sharks?

   _____

5. Write three things about great white sharks.

   _____

   _____

   _____

UNDER THE SEA – BIG AND SMALL

Plankton are tiny fish and plants; some are so small that you can hardly see them. They are eaten by some sorts of whale and fish.

Giant squids have never been caught alive, so we know very little about them. They can be 17 metres long and are the largest animals without bones.

Great white sharks are very fierce and can kill humans. They can be 6 metres long, which is smaller than some sharks. They usually live in warm seas and eat other fish and seals. They have very strong jaws.

The whale shark is enormous, sometimes more than 18 metres long. It is not dangerous, though, as it only eats plankton.

The basking shark is another shark that only eats plankton. It can be 15 metres long. Sharks are not as dangerous as many people think!

Reading for information

Here is information about dangerous snakes. Remember to look at the first sentence of a paragraph to see what the whole paragraph will be about.

Read the information and answer the questions on the next page.

POISONOUS SNAKES

Snakes kill in different ways. Some are poisonous and others squeeze an animal so that it cannot breathe. They do not kill for fun, though – they kill what they want to eat or something that they think will harm them.

Some poisonous snakes are more dangerous than others. The most poisonous snake in the world is the black-headed sea snake. Other very poisonous ones are the krait, the coral snake and the saw-scaled viper. An adder is not very poisonous to a human but you would need to go to hospital if one bit you.

Snakes that kill by squeezing are called constrictors. One, a boa constrictor, could kill a pig. Another well-known constrictor is the python, which can grow up to 2 metres long. Some people keep pythons as pets.

Snakes do not chew their food. When they have killed an animal, they open their jaws very wide and swallow the animal whole. In fact, they can 'unhook' their jaws to open them wider than any other animal.

For your answers, only give information that you can find on page 74. Answer in whole sentences.

1. What are the two ways in which a snake can kill?

_____

2. What is the most poisonous snake in the world?

_____

3. How does a constrictor kill?

_____

4. What sort of snake is a python?

_____

5. Which paragraph is about how snakes eat?

_____

6. Does that page tell us anything about grass snakes?

_____

7. What else would you like to know about snakes which the page does not tell you?

_____

8. How might you find out what you want to know?

_____

Instructions are a type of non-fiction. If instructions are written well, they should be easy to understand. But make sure you read them very carefully. It's always best to read through to the end before you start to follow the instructions.

The teacher is preparing for a show. The parents are making costumes for the children. Because she wants each child to look exactly right, she must write the instructions very clearly.

Dear Parent,

Your child is going to be an elf in our school show. Please could you provide this outfit by next Monday?

- dark green jumper or plain T-shirt (no pictures)
- dark green tights
- brown felt shoes: to make each shoe, take an oval-shaped piece of brown felt about 30 cm wide and 50 cm long; place your child's foot in the middle and gather up the edges and tie with a red ribbon
- red belt
- cardboard hat shaped like an upside-down boat and painted green; with a feather sticking up
- pointed ears (you can get these in the joke shop on Bank Street)
- some sort of purse tied to the belt with a piece of string

Thank you very much,

Miss Strangeways

Miss Strangeways

Now follow those instructions and draw the whole outfit here. Label everything clearly so that your mum or dad knows about colours and details.

Idea: You could design a new outfit for your school football or basketball team. Write all the details very clearly and draw a picture as well.

Letters are another type of non-fiction. There are lots of reasons to write a letter. Letters to strangers must be very polite; letters to close friends can be more chatty.

You might want to: thank your granny for a birthday present

write to a penfriend, telling him/her about yourself

Can you think of four more reasons for writing a letter?

_____

_____

_____

_____

Read the letter on the opposite page.

1. Who wrote it? _____

2. Who is it to?   _____

3. Why has she written this letter? _____

_____

4. Is it written politely? _____

5. If you were writing a postcard to your best friend, how might your

   language be different? _____

_____

14 Orchard View
Wilton
WB4 3RC

12/06/10

Dear Mr Owen,

I am writing to ask whether you would be able to come to our school and talk to us about what it is like to be a professional tennis player. We had a vote in my class and we decided that we would like you to come.

There are lots of questions we would like to ask. How did you become a tennis player? What is training like? Do you have to eat special foods? Are there any other things you would like to do if you were not a tennis player? What is it like to be famous? And what were the worst and the best moments of your life?

I know you are busy but I hope that you can come. If you can, please write to me and let me know.

Thank you very much.

Yours sincerely,

Sally Grey

Sally Grey

Imagine you want to write a letter to an author, because you have enjoyed a book. The notes show some things you might want to say. Think of some more and put them in order. Then write the letter.

your address and the date

Notes

liked book
the title
why I liked it
my name, age
more about me
do you like writing?

_____

_____

_____

_____

_____

_____

_____

Dear ....

Top tip:
Always put *Yours faithfully* if you don't use the person's name and *Yours sincerely* if you do.

You have now nearly finished this section.
Here's a fun exercise to do before you move on to Writing Composition.

Do a survey! What can you discover about your friends' likes and dislikes?
It could be about food, or pop groups, or sports, or anything you like. Or you could
find out what they think about their own futures. Do they think they will
get married, for example?
Write your own questions, and add the names of your friends.
Then put a tick or cross in each square of the grid.

Names

Questions

What does all the information tell you? What were the most or least usual answers?

A paragraph is a group of sentences all about the same thing. The first sentence of each paragraph should say what the rest of the paragraph will be about. When we write about something, we must sort our information into paragraphs.

Here is some information about Vikings:

The Vikings were people who came from Norway, Denmark and Sweden about 1,000 years ago. They came to Britain on their huge ships, looking for more land. They were very fierce and brave fighters.

The Vikings were not just soldiers, though. They were also farmers, poets and musicians. They made clever and beautiful things with metal, leather and wood. They also made wonderful houses and boats.

The Vikings used to buy and sell things. Sometimes they used coins, but usually they did something called 'bartering'. To barter means to swap one thing for another.

The Vikings also used to buy and sell things in foreign countries. This is called 'trading'. The Vikings were very good at this because they could use their excellent ships to take goods to faraway places and then to bring back the things they bought. This meant they could buy things that could not be grown in the cold countries where they lived.

How many paragraphs are there? _____ Underline the first sentence of each.

Look at the first sentence of each paragraph.
The rest of the paragraph tells you something more about that sentence.

The first paragraph could be called 'Who were the Vikings?'
Can you think of a title or heading for the other paragraphs?

Paragraph 2 _____

Paragraph 3 _____

Paragraph 4 _____

Choose a topic and write the headings your paragraphs might have. You can choose one of these topics or think of one of your own.

animals   my family   the Egyptians   football   dinosaurs

Paragraph 1 _____

Paragraph 2 _____

Paragraph 3 _____

Paragraph 4 _____

Now write what your first sentence might be for each paragraph.

Paragraph 1 _____

Paragraph 2 _____

Paragraph 3 _____

Paragraph 4 _____

A story-writer can't just pour out a story like cement from a cement-mixer. The parts of a story have to be built properly and with all the correct parts.

Although all stories are different, they follow a similar pattern. If you understand this, you will find two good things will happen: you will appreciate better the stories you read, and you will be able to write like a real writer yourself!

The pattern is:

Introduction: meet characters, learn important things about the story;

Build-up: the main points of the story are developed so we learn more;

Conflicts: difficulties/adventures for the main character;

Climax: the worst/most difficult point for the main character;

Resolution: what happens in the end.

Think of a story you know. It could be a well-known story like *Cinderella* or it could be the last story you read. Can you break the story into these parts?

Title: _____

Introduction: _____

Build-up: _____

Conflicts (there may be any number): _____

Climax: _____

Resolution: _____

Building an argument

As with stories, arguments must be built properly. A writer can't just put down all his ideas as they come into his head. That would not make a strong argument. A good argument needs planning, so that opinions and facts are in the best order.

There are different ways in which a writer might organise opinions and facts to form an argument. Here is one way that would work well:

Introduction: explain what the argument is about
Point 1: the first point and some facts to support it
Point 2: the second point and some facts
Point 3: (and as many more points as necessary)
Summing-up or Conclusion: reminding the reader of all the points and showing why the writer has this strong opinion

Read this passage and put ⌐ where each part of the argument ends.

Some schools insist that the pupils must wear school uniform, but others do not. I believe that school uniform is a good idea. ⌐ It is much easier for parents. It means that they do not have to have arguments about what their children are wearing. In a survey of parents, 75% said they prefer to have school uniform. Also, it is easier for pupils themselves. Pupils do not have to spend time deciding what to wear each morning. Our survey found that children take ten minutes longer to get dressed when they do not have uniform. School uniform is fairer. Some families have less money and can't afford expensive clothes. Many children complain of being bullied because of this. In short, it is easier and fairer for everyone if school uniform is compulsory.

Can you think of another point that this writer could have made?

_____

The parts of a story must be in a sensible order.
The order in which things happen is called the **sequence**.

This flow-chart shows the sequence
of the story of Cinderella.

Cinderella has cruel
stepmother + sisters

↓

Prince asks all girls in the land
to a ball

↓

Sisters say she can't go –
she is v sad

↓

Fairy Godmother says she can go
and makes magic carriage and dress
But she must leave by midnight or
everything will turn back to normal

↓

At the ball, Prince falls in love with her

↓

Midnight strikes – she rushes off but one
shoe falls off and is left behind

↓

Next day, Prince sends servant
to find owner of shoe

↓

Sisters are furious when it is
Cinderella

↓

Cinderella marries Prince – lives happily
ever after

Make a flow-chart for any
story you know.

_____

_____

_____

_____

_____

_____

_____

_____

_____

_____

_____

_____

_____

_____

When you plan a story, you have to decide what sort of story it will be. It could be a fairy story, a fable or an adventure. It could be funny or frightening, strange or ordinary. The writer decides – that's you!

More than 2,000 years ago, a man called Aesop wrote stories called **fables**. A fable is a story that teaches a lesson. Here is a plan for one of his fables:

Title: The Fox and the Crow

Sort of story: fable

Sequence:

Crow in tree with cheese in beak

fox wants cheese

clever fox has plan

fox says, 'I've heard you sing beautifully.'

silly crow is so proud that he opens his mouth to sing

cheese drops to ground and fox runs off with it

Use the plan to tell the whole story in your own words.

_____

_____

_____

_____

_____

_____

_____

_____

_____

_____

_____

_____

Setting

Setting means **where** and **when** a story takes place. It could be a desert, a forest, a town, a pretend country, a real country or even on the moon. It could be past, present or future, day or night, or at a special time of year.

Example:

Albert Brubdig lived deep in a forest on the mountain of Zorabud. Zorabud, in case you didn't know, is the biggest mountain on the planet of Mib and is a most strange place. He had moved there from Earth in the year 2130.

The setting is a *forest on another planet*. It is *in the future*, the year 2130.

What are the settings of these? See if you can say where and when.

The wind whistled outside as we sat warmly inside our igloo. We wondered whether the Arctic winter would ever end.

_____
_____
_____
_____

That night in the jungle was the most frightening of my life. I imagined every sound was a lion, a rhinoceros, a snake, – all coming to eat me.

_____
_____
_____
_____

Long ago, in the city of London, a young boy sat cleaning the shoes of passing gentlemen. All his life, he had only known the dirt, the crowds, the smells.

_____
_____
_____
_____

Setting

When you are planning a story, decide the setting.
When you start to write, put some details of the setting in the
first paragraph so that the reader can picture the scene.

Imagine you are writing some stories. Here are the
settings. Write a few sentences to show the setting. Put in
lots of details to show **where** and **when**.

Palace: _____

_____

_____

_____

Forest: _____

_____

_____

_____

A pirate ship: _____

_____

_____

_____

Fun idea: Think of a story you know well (maybe a fairy story or Bible story).
Change the setting to your own home and modern times. How will the clothes and
language be different? How would the people behave now?

Character

Characters are **who** the story is about. You need to decide exactly what your characters are like, and tell the reader clearly. Lots of details will help the reader imagine your characters.

Here are some notes about a character from a story that you may know.
Can you work out who it is? _____

What I look like	Where I live	My family	What sort of person
small boy	the jungle	wolves	brave
bare feet	India	other animals	cheeky
a cloth round			naughty
my waist	**Anything else special?**		friendly
scruffy black hair	enemy is a tiger		strong

Do the same for a character from a book you have read.
Can your friends guess who you are describing?

What I look like	Where I live	My family	What sort of person
_____	_____	_____	_____
_____	_____	_____	_____
_____	Anything else special?	_____	_____
_____		_____	_____
_____	_____	_____	_____
_____	_____	_____	_____

Your characters can look and behave any way you want. You are the author, so **you** choose. When you write, describe your character's special details.

Here are lots of ways to describe a person. Add some more ideas.
Choose any of the details and describe a person you have made up.

eyes: small, wide, dark, green, sparkling, tired, _____

mouth: large, heart-shaped, cross, smiling, mean, _____

nose: hooked, snub, button, floppy, wide nostrils, _____

skin: dark, healthy, red, blotchy, smooth, wrinkled, _____

hair: long, curly, straight, frizzy, dark, shiny, scruffy, _____ _____

shape: tall, short, slim, plump, strong, _____ _____

personality: grumpy, friendly, cruel, helpful, warm, _____

extra details: walks with a limp, always stares, squeaky voice,

_____

_____

Describe the person here:

_____

_____

_____

_____

_____

Draw the person:

We can do special things with words to make the reader feel something.
You might want to make the reader frightened, or happy, or even sad.
Or you might just want to make the reader imagine exactly what you want.
One way to do this is to choose your words **very** carefully.

In this poem, I have underlined words that make you think of *fast*, *light* things, because this is what I want you to imagine.

<u>Fins flicking</u> like <u>feather fans</u>
<u>Faster</u> than <u>blinking</u> the fish <u>flit</u>.
<u>Turning</u> here, there — now nowhere
They have gone
Leaving <u>fizzy bubbles</u> full of <u>air</u>.

Make a list of words you might choose if you were writing about:

an elephant	a desert	a snake
_____	_____	_____
_____	_____	_____
_____	_____	_____
_____	_____	_____
_____	_____	_____
_____	_____	_____
_____	_____	_____

Here is a special way to choose words. It is called **alliteration**. Alliteration is when we choose some words that start with the same sound.

Examples:

The dormouse darted into the darkness of its den.

Bumble bees buzzed among the bluebells.

The snow turned slowly to sludge and slush.

Here are some words. For each, think of two more that start with the same sound and put them all together in a sentence. The first is done for you.

clattered: the horse *clattered* and *crashed* in the *courtyard*

sausages: _____

witch: _____

wind: _____

dog: _____

boat: _____

balloon: _____

snake: _____

boy: _____

Top tip:

It doesn't have to be the same *letter*, just the sound. So, 'sad <u>C</u>inderella <u>s</u>ings' is alliteration, too.

More special effects with words

Some words are special because they **sound** like their **meaning**.
These are useful when we want to describe a noise. We call this **onomatopoeia**.

Examples:
The raindrops went *drip, drip, drip, drip*. (Listen to the sound of the word.)
The tree fell with a *thud*.
She *screeched* with horror.

Choose the best word to fill each space.
When you have chosen a word, say it out loud and listen to how it sounds.

1. The glass broke in pieces with a _____ (thud/crash/thump).

2. The thunder _____ (roared/tinkled/whistled).

3. The stream _____ (moaned/crashed/trickled) over the pebbles.

4. The bird _____ (cheeped/squealed/roared) to its mother.

5. Our boots _____ (thudded/squelched/clattered) in the mud.

6. Her shoes went _____ (clack/thump/bash) on the stone floor.

7. There was a _____ (squelch/crash/click) as I switched on the lamp.

8. The saucepan lid _____ (plopped/tinkled/clanged) on the floor.

What words would be good to describe the noises of these?

Water falling   Animals calling   A snake moving   Someone eating

_____   _____   _____   _____

_____   _____   _____   _____

_____   _____   _____   _____

Usually, we try to have some short and some long sentences. This is more interesting to read. But sometimes it is interesting to use a string of short sentences. They can show a very exciting part of a story.

Read these short sentences. How do they make you feel?

The footsteps were getting closer now. Why was there no one to help me?
I started to run. My heart was racing. My lungs hurt. I could hear it behind me.
Right behind me. I could hear the growling. I screamed. Aaagh!

Turn this passage into lots of short sentences.
You need to cut out a few small words and put full stops in.

This was the most important race of my life and I could see the finishing line.
I was in the lead but I knew someone was close behind me and I mustn't look round. My mouth was open and my lungs were gasping for breath.
I couldn't run any faster but I had to win so I must go faster. Suddenly
I realised that I was over the line and I had won.

_____
_____
_____
_____
_____
_____
_____

Read your version aloud. How does it sound different?

Starting our story

What do you think is the most important part of a story? It's the **beginning**, because if the first paragraph is boring the reader might not read the rest.

Your first paragraph should: show the setting
show what sort of story it is
make the reader want to read on

Read this first paragraph.

Tom was woken by the sound of creaking wood and the fact that his bed was swaying. Where was he? Voices yelled in the distance and a seagull screeched. A seagull and a swaying bed – he must be on a ship. He touched his head and felt a bump under his thick, black hair. Ouch! Now he remembered – pirates, fighting, being caught and tied up as he struggled bravely. Tom heard footsteps outside. His heart thumped like a drum.
The door opened.

Does this make you want to read further? _____

Why? _____

Circle what sort of story you think it will be: Fairy   Ghost   Adventure

What is the setting? _____

What is Tom like? _____

What else does this first paragraph tell you? _____

_____

_____

Write the first paragraph for these stories. Use the ideas box to write down ideas before you start to write.

A ghost story set in your town, with a kind old lady.

Ideas

_____

_____

_____

_____

_____

Ideas

An adventure set in the future, about a family going to space.

_____

_____

_____

_____

_____

A story for very young children, about a lion who is always frightened.

Ideas

_____

_____

_____

_____

We can use poetic language in all sorts of writing, not just poems. When you write a poem or use poetic language, you try to choose the words very carefully, to make your writing strong and beautiful.

This is not poetic: The lion was fierce.

What about this?   Blazing, furious, fierce, fuming,

The lion paces round with roaring eyes

Like fire, and snarls with massive features looming

Over the people watching him. Watching them.

As well as alliteration, which you have looked at on page 93, this poem also contains a simile.

Simile: when something is said to be 'like' or 'as' something else.

e.g. as loud as thunder, eyes like saucers. Underline the simile in the poem.

Write a short descriptive poem about one of these: custard, rain, a gorilla, sand, snakes, wind. Can you include alliteration and a simile?

_____

_____

_____

_____

_____

_____

_____

_____

Writing poems

Writing poems is fun and a very useful way to practise using language. Although they are usually shorter than stories, they take just as much care. A poem's idea can be very simple, but every word must be exactly right.

Practise writing some poems here. I've suggested some first lines to help you start. See if you can use some alliteration and similes, as well as beautifully chosen adjectives, verbs and adverbs.

The sea is calm tonight

The snow falls deep;
the forest lies alone

I wandered lonely as a cloud

Tiger! Tiger! Burning bright

Top tip:
These first lines are all the beginnings of famous poems. Can you find them in a library? Ask the librarian how to find them.

More writing poems

How about a shape poem, where you make your lines have the shape of the thing your poem is about?

The Huge Old
Oak Tree

_____
_____
_____
_____
_____
_____

Words I want to use

_____
_____
_____
_____
_____
_____

Snowy Mountain

_____
_____
_____
_____
_____

Words I want to use

_____
_____
_____
_____
_____
_____
_____

A poem could tell a story, too. A story poem needs a setting, just like any story.

Write a poem about the Vikings. Page 82 tells you about Vikings but you can also imagine or look up some more details.

The Vikings are Coming!

_____

_____

_____

_____

_____

_____

_____

_____

_____

Ideas and words:

fierce, frightening, fire
swords, slicing, spears
rough, cold, noisy songs
huge ships, sailing
stormy seas
brave, bold, beards
heave ho, land ho, yo ho
people run away

_____

_____

_____

_____

Top tip:

Write a noun vertically down the page, e.g. dogs. Try to write a poem about that noun by starting each new line with the next letter in the word.

d _____

o _____

g _____

s _____

Non-fiction: making notes

We can find information from books, television or computers.
Or we might ask someone who knows about the topic.

But we can't just copy. First we make notes.
Then we write using our own words.
Making notes means writing down the **main words** or **facts**.
Notes do not have to be proper sentences.

Look again at the information about Vikings on page 82.
These are the notes I used before I wrote paragraph 1:

Vikings – from Norway, Denmark and Sweden – about 1,000 years ago.
To Britain – huge ships, wanting land. Very fierce + brave fighters.

Can you make notes for the other paragraphs?

Paragraph 2 _____

_____

_____

Paragraph 3 _____

_____

_____

Paragraph 4 _____

_____

_____

_____

Non-fiction: making notes

When you make notes and plan paragraphs, two good things will happen. First, writing it up will be much easier, because you just follow your notes. Second, your teacher will be very pleased because your work will be easy to understand and well organised.

On page 83 you chose a topic and planned what your paragraphs might be about. You can carry on with the same topic or choose another if you wish.

My topic: _____

Paragraph 1 Heading: _____

Notes: _____

_____

Paragraph 2 Heading: _____

Notes: _____

_____

Paragraph 3 Heading: _____

Notes: _____

_____

Paragraph 4 Heading: _____

Notes: _____

_____

If you would like another paragraph, write here:

Paragraph 5 Heading: _____

Notes: _____

_____

Sometimes you collect information from lots of different places. Then you have to sort all the points into paragraphs or sections and decide an order for presenting the information.

I've made lots of notes about Henry VIII. I found the information in different books, and also on the Internet, so it's all muddled up.

Dates: 1509-1547
Very cruel.
Liked eating, riding, music, hunting and fighting.
Six wives: 1. Catherine of Aragon (Spanish), divorced.
2. Anne Boleyn, executed. 3. Jane Seymour (favourite, only one who gave him son to succeed him), died.
4. Anne of Cleves, divorced. 5. Catherine Howard, executed. 6. Catherine Parr, only one still around when H. died. Divorced Anne of Cleves – because ugly!
Wrote songs, played musical instruments.
Very large.
Married Catherine Parr though she was engaged to someone else.
Had Thomas More executed for disagreeing – then boiled his head and stuck it on pole.
Refused to go to daughter's christening.
Did what wanted. If people got in way, executed them.
Had party to celebrate first wife's death.
Hated not getting his way.
Had to have armour made specially, as so big.
The Pope wouldn't let him divorce first wife, so H. left the Catholic church.

Here are the headings you might use to sort the information on page 104:

Underline in red the facts which would go under the first heading.
Underline in blue the facts which would go under the second heading.
Underline in green the facts which would go under the third heading.
If something could fit two headings, choose the one you think is better.
Finally, write key words or phrases in the spaces by each heading.

Henry's likes, dislikes

_____

_____

Henry's cruelty

_____

_____

Henry's wives

_____

_____

Other facts

_____

_____

_____

_____

_____

Writing information from notes

Now it is time to practise all you have learnt about making notes and planning.

Here is some information about jumbo jets. There are some paragraph headings on the next page. Make notes for each paragraph. Then use your notes to write clearly about jumbo jets.

Jumbo jets are the biggest planes in the world. The word 'jumbo' means elephant.

They are so big that they often have an upstairs and a downstairs. Some have bedrooms and showers.

Some jumbo jets can carry more than 400 passengers because they are so big.

A pilot has many years of training. He must learn to work hundreds of different buttons in the flight deck.

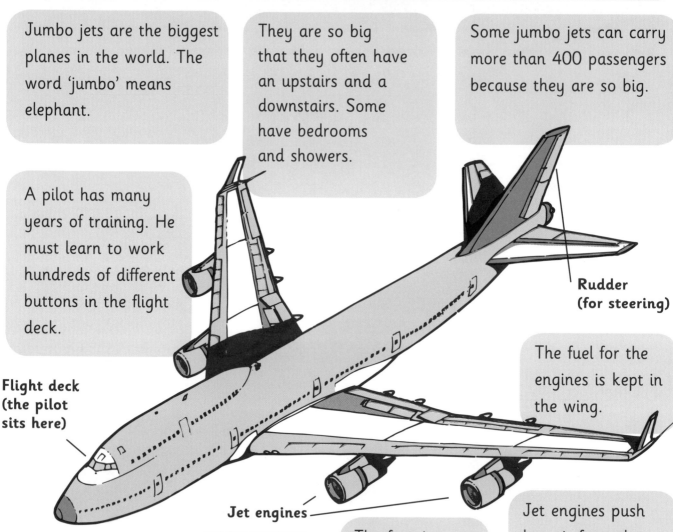

Rudder
(for steering)

The fuel for the engines is kept in the wing.

Flight deck
(the pilot
sits here)

Jet engines

The pilot uses a radio to speak to a controller on the ground.

Computers tell the pilot how high and how fast he is flying.

The four jet engines can make the plane fly at 900 kilometres an hour.

Jet engines push hot air from the back of the engine. This makes the plane go forwards.

Paragraph 1: <u>how big jumbo jets are</u>

Notes: _____

_____

Paragraph 2: <u>the pilot</u>

Notes: _____

_____

Paragraph 3: <u>jet engines</u>

Notes: _____

_____

Now use your notes to write the piece in full sentences and paragraphs.

_____

_____

_____

_____

_____

_____

_____

Persuasive writing is when you try to persuade others to agree with you. Sorting your ideas is just as important as when writing information. Planning will help make your argument more persuasive. We call it an argument, but this does not mean shouting!

Use your planning skills to structure your argument well.

Introduction – outlining what you are going to talk about;

Point 1 – and some reasons or facts to support it;

Point 2 – and some reasons or facts to support it;

Points 3, 4 ... (or however many points you want);

Conclusion – summing-up your points and making sure your argument is clear.

But before you can organise your points, you need to jot down ideas as you think of them.

Choose one of these topics, or any other topic which interests you:

- Hunting foxes should be banned;
- Children should work for their pocket money;
- Children should choose their bedtime;
- There should be no school rules.

Jot down your ideas in any order. Include any information and facts you can.

Planning to persuade

Top tip:
When giving your opinion, you can also mention what someone on the other side might say and explain why you disagree with it.

Once you have jotted down your ideas, make some headings and then put key words and phrases under the correct headings.

Don't write the whole sentences – just notes!

Introduction: _____

Point 1: _____

Point 2: _____

Point 3: _____

Conclusion/summing-up: _____

On the previous pages you saw how to make notes and organise your opinions to form a strong and persuasive argument.

You need to choose the right style and vocabulary, too. If you follow these tips, your argument will be more persuasive:

- don't be rude to people on the other side of the argument;
- choose strong words to encourage people to agree with you;
- think about who your reader is and choose the language and style to fit;
- say enough, but not too much (or your reader may be bored).

Imagine this: Your new head teacher believes that you should do an hour's homework every night. You disagree, so you decide to write to her.

First you need to plan your argument.

Introduction: why I am writing

Point 1: _____

Point 2: _____

Point 3: _____

Conclusion: _____

Some ideas: we work hard all day – need to relax – after-school activities are very good for us – sometimes the homework is not helpful – some parents help too much – need to practise musical instrument – some children have long journey home.

Use your notes to write to the head teacher giving your views.

Turn the notes into good sentences, using stronger words where you can.

Each new point should have a new paragraph.

Your address here

Date here

Teacher's address

Dear . . . . ,

Yours sincerely,

Your signature

Lists

Sometimes instructions and lists go together. A good example is in a recipe. A recipe has a list of all the things you need. Then it has very clear instructions so that the reader will know exactly what to do.

Here are the instructions for making a cake.
Make a list of everything you would need.
Put the things in the order you would need them.

1. Ask a grown-up to turn the oven on. Line a cake tin with baking paper.
2. In a large bowl, beat 100g of sugar and 100g of butter with a wooden spoon until it goes pale and creamy.
3. In a small bowl, beat two eggs well with a fork.
4. Slowly add the eggs to the butter and sugar, beating all the time.
5. Sieve 100g of self-raising flour and a pinch of salt into the mixture.
6. Gently mix with a metal spoon.
7. Pour into cake tin and bake for about 25 minutes, until golden and firm.

Ingredients	Kitchen equipment	
	Oven	

Lists

Sometimes it's good to make lists before you write something.
For example, you might be asked to say whether something is good or bad.
Making lists of good points and bad points would help you to plan this.

Example:

My school is trying to decide whether to spend money on new football kits
for the teams. I asked my class to write what they thought about this.
These were their ideas.

Reasons for having new kits

the old ones are torn

the teams look scruffy

the teams would feel proud

other schools look smarter

Reasons against having new kits

too expensive

lots of children don't play in the teams

could buy gym equipment instead

people could buy their own

Think of something you or your family or your school would like to buy.
Can you make lists of reasons for and against buying that thing?

Reasons for buying _____

Reasons against buying _____

_____

_____

_____

_____

_____

_____

_____

_____

_____

_____

Instructions and rules

Instructions and rules don't need paragraphs. You can write them like a list, perhaps with numbers. The information must be very clear to understand.

Always put instructions or rules in the right order.

Here are the instructions for working my television. Are they in the best order? Put numbers in the boxes to show a better order.

☐ Watch the programme.

☐ Select the channel you want.

☐ Make sure the television is plugged in.

☐ Press the ON / OFF button.

Here are the rules for playing one sort of 'Tig'.
Put them in the correct order to make sense.

☐ If someone has been 'tigged', they must not move until set free by someone else. You free people by crawling under their legs.

☐ Everyone runs away from the person who has been chosen.

☐ Choose one person to be 'it'.

☐ The person who is 'it' has to chase the others. To 'tig' someone, the person who is 'it' must touch an arm.

Instructions and rules

You can write some instructions yourself now. Imagine that a visitor has come from another planet and needs to know how to go shopping. There are no shops on his planet so he doesn't know anything at all about shops or money or what you say when you are in a shop.

First make some notes: jot everything down that you can think of, in any order. Then put everything into the best order for your visitor to understand.

Notes	Instructions

Writing information from a flow-chart

Another way of writing instructions is something called a flow-chart.
A flow-chart uses arrows to show what to do next.

This flow-chart shows how to go from my house to the Post Office.
Make sure you follow the direction of the arrows.

Go out of my door and turn right.	→	At the second corner turn left.	→	Go on for 100 metres.

You will see the Post Office.	←	Cross the road at the lights.	←	Turn right at the letter box.

Write these instructions as a numbered list:

1. _____

2. _____

3. _____

4. _____

5. _____

6. _____

You can also use a flow-chart as your plan before you write about something. The important thing about a flow-chart is to follow the arrows carefully.

This flow-chart shows how glass is made. Using the notes in it, write one paragraph of proper sentences, to explain how a glass jar is made.

Sand, limestone and ash are melted in very hot oven	when very hot, becomes liquid	liquid poured into jar-shaped mould
machine pushes air into it, forcing glass up the sides	jar is put in special oven, making it tougher	when jar is cold, it sets and is ready

How a glass jar is made

_____

_____

_____

_____

_____

_____

You can use these pages to plan and write about anything you like. You will need to find information about your topic. Think about what books you have. Perhaps you could go to the library.

Here are some ideas:
dinosaurs, a foreign country, deserts, space, television, football.

Remember: you need to make notes and plan your paragraphs.

Notes: _____

_____

_____

_____

_____

_____

_____

_____

_____

Paragraph 1 _____

Paragraph 2 _____

Paragraph 3 _____

Paragraph 4 _____

Paragraph 5 _____

Decide how many paragraphs you need.

You can write your piece here. Follow your plan carefully.

You have now nearly finished this section and the whole Mega English book!

Below are three character and story outlines. Choose one, and write a story bringing together all of the things you have learnt in this book. Think carefully about the characters, setting, any dialogue they might use and how the story might end. You can plan the story using notes, a list or even a flow-chart.

Think about your language too, using powerful verbs and adjectives, similes and alliteration. And don't forget to check your work carefully at the end.

Have fun! Enjoy being the author and let your imagination run free!

Sophie:
brilliant at music,
has a very sad past,
wants to be a dancer.

Sally:
very confident,
lazy, boastful,
wants to be a musician.

Sarah:
very shy,
dyslexic,
wants to be a writer.

1
This thrilling story, set in a drama school, is about how one girl overcomes tragedy and difficulty to achieve her aims.

2
The exciting story of a girl who eventually learns that you don't just need talent – but hard work, too. At the same time, she learns that we all need friends.

3
The moving story of one girl's battle against difficulties. She finds a hidden talent, when a friend secretly enters her for a drama competition. Although terrified, she agrees to go ahead.

You have learnt lots of ways of making your writing more powerful.
But there's one more important thing: you need to check what you have
written, to try to avoid little mistakes.
Spelling, punctuation and using exactly the right words are all
important – they help readers enjoy your work.

How many mistakes can you find in this passage?

Jake was brilliant at everything and he knew it? When Mr Hogly was choosing a

team, you could be sure Jake would be captin. If their was a compitition, weather

it was writing peoms, desinging a poster, or playing an instrument, you could be

equaly shore that Jake would win it.

Off course, the teechers loved Jake, he sat class like an angel, listening carfully,

answering questions, always handing in his homework on time. Jake would never

be caught passing notes or poking someone else in the back when teacher was'nt

looking. There was something that the teachers didn't know about jake, though.

Something which they would very much like to have known, although they might

not have beleived it.

GRAMMAR and PUNCTUATION

page 4
Underline the common nouns:
 country city factories machines world televisions washing-machines cameras computers cars rice farmers wheat barley soya restaurants countries dishes fish vegetables

Circle the proper nouns:
 Japan
 Asia
 Tokyo
 Japan
 Japan

page 5
Circle the collective nouns:
 bunch swarm pack group herd shoal flock team

Put the correct collective noun in each space:
 a pack of wolves,
 a bunch of bananas,
 a swarm of bees,
 a team of footballers,
 a flock of birds

page 6
Fill in these spaces:
 ships, bushes, tomato, sheep

Write the plural:
 I saw cats eat ice creams while waiting for buses.
 Have you ever seen potatoes with eyes that blinked?
 The burglars hid the watches behind bushes. (or some bushes)
 She picked up the lambs and the sheep followed her home.

page 7
Fill in these spaces: children, calves, man, loaves, huff
Write the plural:
 The wolves took huge puffs but couldn't blow the houses down.
 The men needed hot knives to fit shoes to the pony's hooves.
 I put my feet in my trousers and caught my toes on the buttons.

page 8
 Walking along my street, I saw an old lady. She looked in pain. I asked her if I could do anything to help. She asked me to phone her son.
 I phoned him and he asked me where she was. I told him that she was by the supermarket. It was the one she always went to so he knew where to find her.

page 9
Put a possessive pronoun in the spaces:
 I. his, his
 2. her
 3. their
 4. our
 5. my
 6. mine
 7. your

page 10
 Any verbs that make sense score one mark. Extra points for descriptive verbs such as:
 battered, whistled, screeched, charged, hurtled, trembled, shook, slithered, darted, leapt, pounced, appeared, scrambled, clambered, scampered, escape (or any others that you are very pleased with).

page II
Here are some words that mean said:
 I. shouted
 2. replied
 3. asked
 4. whispered
 5. screamed
Can you think of 5 words to use instead of go:
 examples – depart, leave, set off, set out, withdraw, visit, proceed (you might think of others).

page 12
 I. ran, screamed – past, past
 2. will do – future
 3. hurts, touch – present, present
 4. am watching, can't come – present, present
 5. went – past
 6. rains, love – present, present
 7. will shrink, has drunk – future, past

page I3
Turn these into the past tense:
 I. She hopped faster than her brother but he jumped higher.
 2. I wanted to go out.
 3. Jody laughed as she looked down at her filthy clothes.
 4. As we walked along the beach, the sea lapped at our feet. (or, 'as we were walking ... the sea was lapping')

Answers

What is the past tense of these verbs?

talked, trickled, hoped, climbed, wanted, allowed, died

page 14

was wandering (or wandered) – looked – screamed – started – screamed (or were screaming) – didn't (or did not) seem – started – was happening – shouted (or were shouting) – realised – believed – was

page 15

Turn these into the 1st person plural: We climbed Mount Everest. We helped at the school play. We are going to Spain next year.
Turn these into the second person: You shouldn't have done that. You are good at football. You were happy to go home.

page 16

had – past; missed – past; were – past; heard – past; slid/flashed (eg) – past; come – present; said – past; will – future; is – present; love – present; won't – future

page 17

1. had
2. was
3. fought
4. won
5. did
6. taught
7. thought, could
8. stole
9. ate
10. caught
11. made
12. bought
13. spoke
14. heard
15. swam
16. ran

page 18

1. lumbered
2. trickled
3. yelled
4. limped
5. slumped
6. shot

page 19

(any appropriate answers)

page 20

Any adjectives that make sense. Score one point for every adjective. Score 2 points if it was a really good one. Score 3 if you thought of one yourself. Take one point away if you used the same word twice.

page 21

Score one point for each colour that you think of.

page 22

(Although these are the answers we expect, if you really think a different answer is better, give good reasons and you can have a point!) bad – good – good – bad – good – bad – bad – good

page 23

No right or wrong answers. Think about whether you are happy with your choices.

page 24

quick, quicker, quickest;
brave, braver, bravest;
thin, thinner, thinnest;
large, larger, largest;
fast, faster, fastest;
good, better, best;
bad, worse, worst

page 25

1. most skilful
2. more painful
3. most terrible
4. most horrifying
5. more intelligent
6. more experienced
7. most brilliant
8. more ridiculous

page 26

thrilled, pleased, content
gigantic, huge, large
grotesque, unattractive, plain
scorching, steaming, warm

page 27

1. perfectly round and clear
2. with black spots
3. much too frightening
4. very expensively decorated
5. with plenty of excitement
6. with fairly simple rules
7. too small for our family
8. the smallest imaginable
9. red with a green stripe down the middle
10. all covered in leaves and mud

page 28

We went to Greece last July. It was as hot as a desert. Have you ever been?
We stayed in a house on a mountain. What do you think was the best thing about the house? It was the swimming pool. It was so blue and beautifully refreshing after a hot day at the beach. We liked the Greek food. The tomatoes were the biggest I have ever seen.

page 29

1. <u>I took her to the doctor</u>, who said she would be fine.
2. With a huge leap, <u>the kangaroo jumped out of its cage</u>.
3. If I had a million pounds, <u>I would love to go round the world</u>.
4. <u>Rome is the capital of Italy</u>, which is in Europe.
5. <u>I prefer the red one</u>, even though it is quite old.

page 30

1. <u>I don't want to go</u>, if you're not.
2. <u>She ran down the street</u>, dragging her shopping behind her.
3. With a deafening crash, <u>the great tree fell to the ground</u>.
4. Hoping for a bone, <u>the dog sat outside the butcher's shop</u>.
5. <u>I looked carefully at his face</u>, waiting for some sign of recognition.
6. Without her help, <u>I could never have managed it</u>.
7. Shielding our eyes from the heat, <u>we roasted chestnuts on the bonfire</u>.

8. Blushing a deep purple colour, <u>she managed to recite her poem</u>.

page 31

1. The man, clutching his bag tightly, shouted at the thieves.
2. A tree, swaying violently in the wind, suddenly fell onto the road.
3. An enormous creature, covered in mud and dripping with water, appeared out of the mist.
4. Millions of people, even quite old ones, are learning to use computers.
5. My last thought, just before I fell asleep, was how much I was dreading tomorrow.

In the first one, the boy stole the money. In the second one, the man stole it.

page 32

1. I want to be an athlete; I'm going to go on a special course in the summer.
2. The sun shone through a milky haze; it was still too cold for me.
3. Straining my eyes in the fog, I could just see the hut. I wondered if we could reach it before darkness.
4. I liked the one with pink ears; the one which had a patch on its eye; both the ones with black spots and whiskers; and the one with the fluffiest tail.
5. I want you to investigate how the people in the rainforest live; what their houses are like; what they eat; what they wear; what sorts of technology they have; and what medicines they use.

page 33

1. I was quite amazed: there was money all over the path.
2. The sun was blazing down; there wasn't a cloud to be seen.
3. I want to be an astronaut: I think it would be very exciting.
4. I decided I would go: it would be better than staying indoors.
5. The mist swirled around our feet; it made everything seem eerie.
6. I gasped in horror: there was a face at the window. It grinned at me.
7. Most plants grow better in warm places: the sun helps them grow.

page 34

1. I'll
2. should've
3. She's, I've
4. We're
5. That's, hadn't
6. shouldn't
7. you'll
8. won't, you're

page 35

Check contractions by looking at the list on page 34. If you have any that are not there, check with a grown-up. Make sure n't has the apostrophe in the right place.

page 36

1. my mum's car
2. Sarah's house
3. the teacher's mistake
4. the horses' tails
5. ladies' shoes
6. today's news

7. this driver's fault
8. a doctor's coat
9. the cats' tails
10. my bike's brakes
11. my dad's office
12. my friend's hair

'Apples are healthy' and 'I like sausages best' do not need an apostrophe.

page 37
1. the men's room
2. James' job
3. a children's entertainer
4. women's clothes
5. Mrs Jones' car
6. a baby's pram
7. I left Sarah's at 4 o'clock
8. Isn't that car your mum's?
9. Helen's is a very strange hairstyle
10. their wives' jobs
11. The colours of Joseph's coat were extraordinary

page 38
1. Jim's car is much smarter than ours.
2. Theirs is much more comfortable than his.
3. A lorry has shed its load in the middle of our road.
4. It's quite astonishing how much food he can eat.
5. Have you seen how hard it's snowing?
6. The tree lost most of its branches in the storm.
7. The man said he was a friend of ours.
8. An old woman with bright eyes came right over to where the boys sat.

page 39
1. I ran gasping to my uncle's house.
2. There's a terrible monster who lives in that cave.
3. The Vikings' ships invaded Britain a thousand years ago.
4. The ancient Greeks worshipped many different gods.
5. James' brother was our school's best runner.
6. We often go round to Mrs Black's for a meal.
7. My sisters like pizza but I prefer Chinese meals.
8. Children's meals should be full of energy and goodness.
9. The men's quiz team came equal with the women's.
10. The submarines' sharp grey noses reared from the water like sharks' fins.

page 40
circum = round
bi = two, twice
pre = before
ex = out of, from
poly = many
disagree = not agree, say the opposite
impolite = not polite, rude
irregular = not regular, not normal
misunderstand = not understand

page 41
1. useless
2. lovely
3. famous
4. hopeful
5. lioness
6. waiter
7. hostess
   wonderful
8. coldness

page 42
Your answer might be slightly different from these but ask a grown-up about it. Your answer must NOT contain the word you are explaining.
carpet = a soft covering for a floor
whisper = talk in a quiet voice
pencil = thing for writing with, which can be rubbed out
saucepan = cooking pot
climb = go up
hop = jump on one foot
slower = opposite of faster

page 43
Your answers do not need to be exactly the same.
terrible = awful, dreadful, very bad
beds = soil where plants grow
peculiar = strange, odd, weird
deal = cope with, solve, get rid of
sum = amount of money
agreed = said he would, said yes
refuse = will not, won't, say you won't do something
returned = came back

page 44
Any clear definitions.
What are these?
1. shed/hut
2. rubber/eraser
3. custard

page 45
Any clear definitions. They must have the right endings. Example: For champions, the definition could be 'Winners of competitions', not 'A winner of a competition'.
4 and 8 should be in the past tense.

page 46
awful,
beautiful,
cruel,
furious,
Greek,
invisible,
jealous,
lonely,
miserable

page 47
acts = behaves,
does things
adore = love, like, enjoy
care = mind
complained = moaned,
said crossly, whined
darted = ran, nipped
disappear = go away
leapt = jumped
responded = replied, answered

page 48
Alphabetical order of all the
words is: plink, plumage,
plummet, pluvial, pockmarked,
pointillism, polka, pollywog,
polyp, pomp

READING
COMPREHENSION

page 51
1. The poem has short lines
   and each line starts with a
   capital. The story has lines
   that end when the page
   ends.
2. Each of the words rhymes
   with another line.
3. the story
4. The poem has a beat/
   rhythm/ pattern.
   The story does not.

page 52
1. 3

2. in a restaurant/fast
   food place
3. (A man and a woman are
   sitting in a restaurant);
   (He shouts very loudly);
   (Coming over very slowly
   and looking cross.)
4. once
5. anything reasonable

page 53
Matching books: A: My
Dictionary B: Deserts
and Forests, A Children's
Encyclopedia C: Life in Ancient
Rome D: Famous Inventions,
A Children's Encyclopedia
E: My Dictionary F: A
Children's Encyclopedia
1. An encyclopedia tells you a
bit about lots of things. A book
about dinosaurs would only tell
you about dinosaurs.
2. An encyclopedia.
3. I would need another book.

page 54
opinion, opinion, fact, fiction,
fact, opinion, fact, fiction,
opinion

page 55
1. Smoking often causes
   serious illness. It sometimes
   kills. Passive smoking
   means breathing in
   the smoke from other
   people's cigarettes. Some
   restaurants already ban
   smoking. Many public
   places, such as trains and
   buses also have rules about
   smoking.
2. Everyone who smokes will
   die from it.
3. To make the argument
   seem stronger.
4. The Government must ban
   smoking in public places.

The only places where
people should be allowed
to smoke is in their own
homes.
5. No.
If today is Monday,
tomorrow is Tuesday.
There are 100 centimetres
in a metre.

page 57
1. in a forest
2. huge/dark/tall/trees/snow/
   strong wind
3. a long time ago, before
   Christmas, evening
4. A and C

page 59
1. Five
2. He is friendly. He is good
   and kind, and likes to help
   people who deserve it.
   He has special magic
   powers and is quite funny.
3. (anything that fits the story,
   so that Hans does get the
   grinder)

page 61
1. B
2. C
3. He is rich/mean/unkind/not
   generous/greedy/jealous/
   always wants more.
4. She doesn't complain/she
   is a happy person/she is
   friendly and being kind
   to Hans.

page 63
1. Hans' brother
2. That you shouldn't be
   greedy/that you shouldn't
   steal/that you may be
   punished if you are bad
3. Either: yes, because they
   were poor and they worked
   very hard; they are good
   people and they deserve to

be happy. Or: no, because then they might become greedy, too; people might be jealous of them; I am glad they had the grinder for a while but I think they should not have it for ever.

4. whichever ending you like
5. (any)

page 65
1. B
2. it had eyes like fire, it was dangerous, it had claws
3. whiffling – could be roaring, charging, growling (anything that fits the poem)   tulgey – could be frightening, dark, deep, spooky (anything that fits)
4. C
5. (anything)

page 66
1. she was eaten by the tiger
2. no.
3. yes.

page 67
1. (any 3) sleeping, snoring, playing, fun
2. Verse 1: blue/clear-blue Verse 2: black
3. Yesterday the sea was sleeping, Snoring softly in the sun
4. (any 6) angry, fuming, furious, growling, lashes, crashes, smashes, spitting
5. Yesterday it was calm and quiet with small waves. Today it is rough, loud and with big waves.

page 68
1. One.
2. With.
3. West, nest; shine, mine; flower, bower; delight, night.

4. No.
5. No, it's different.
6. Peaceful.

page 69
Who has seen the wind?
A B C B A D E D
A child should always: **A A B B**
Poem on p 68 **A B A B C C D D** The poem with rhyming couplets is the one by Stevenson.

page 70
1. stare
2. site
3. sauce
4. small loose bits of stone
5. where something begins
6. sprint goes after source
7. sense goes after sauce
8. surgeon goes last

page 71
1. 16 – 19
2. 2 – 5
3. 20 – 24
4. 6 – 10
5. 11 – 15
6. things about baby sharks/ how sharks have babies

page 72
1. circle paragraphs that start The whale shark, Great white sharks and The basking shark.
2. Whale shark and basking shark
3. tiny fish and plants.
4. Great white sharks

5. any three of these: very fierce/can kill humans/up to 6 metres long/smaller than some sharks/live in warm seas/eat fish and seals/very strong jaws

page 75
Your sentences should include these facts:
1. poisoning or crushing/ squeezing
2. black-headed sea snake
3. squeezes an animal so it can't breathe
4. a constrictor
5. fourth/last paragraph
6. No
7. (anything)
8. look in an encyclopedia/find another book about snakes/ look in a computer or on the Internet/ask someone who knows

page 78
Reasons for writing a letter: invite someone to stay/thank someone for returning the purse which you lost/ ask a question/write to someone in hospital/ anything else sensible
1. Sally Grey
2. Mr Owen
3. to ask him to come and talk to her school
4. Yes – she says 'thank you very much' and 'yours sincerely'
5. It would be more chatty and not so polite. I would tell my news and I would put 'love from'.

WRITING COMPOSITION

In this section, most of the answers are only ideas. Your answers may be different. Ask a grown-up.

page 82

4 paragraphs

page 83

Paragraph 2: What else the Vikings did
Paragraph 3: Buying and selling
Paragraph 4: Trading with other countries

page 88

igloo in the Arctic during winter
jungle at night
London long ago

page 90

Mowgli

page 94

1. crash   2. roared
3. trickled   4. cheeped
5. squelched   6. clack
7. click   8. clanged

page 95

This was the most important race of my life. I could see the finishing line. I was in the lead. I knew someone was close behind me. I mustn't look round. My mouth was open. My lungs were gasping for breath. I couldn't run any faster. I had to win. I must go faster. Suddenly I realised that I was over the line. I had won.

It is more exciting.

page 96

1. Yes
2. Because it is exciting/ because I want to know what happens.
3. Adventure.
4. In bed in a wooden ship, in the morning
5. He has thick black hair and he is brave.
6. Tom has been captured after a fight with pirates. He was hurt as he struggled. Someone is coming to the door – probably the pirates.

page 102

2: not just soldiers – farmers, poets, musicians – good at making things from metal, leather, wood – very good houses + boats
3: buying and selling – coins or bartering (swapping)
4: trading – buying and selling in other countries – had good ships so could trade in faraway lands – so could buy things they couldn't get at home

page 112

Ingredients: 100g sugar, 100g butter, 2 eggs, 100g self-raising flour, pinch of salt
Equipment: cake tin, baking paper, large bowl, wooden spoon, small bowl, fork, sieve, metal spoon

page 114

4. Watch the programme.
3. Select the channel you want.
1. Make sure the television is plugged in.
2. Press the ON / OFF button.

4. If someone has been 'tigged', he or she must not move until set free by someone else. You free

people by crawling under their legs.
3. Everyone runs away from the person who has been chosen.
1. Choose one person to be 'it'.
2. The person who is 'it' has to chase the others. To 'tig' someone, the person who is 'it' must touch an arm.

page 116

1. Go out of my door and turn right.
2. At the second corner turn left.
3. Go on for 100 metres.
4. Turn right at the letter box.
5. Cross the road at the lights.
6. You will see the Post Office.

page 117

Anything reasonable.

page 121

Jake was brilliant at everything and he knew it. When Mr Hogly was choosing a team, you could be sure Jake would be captain. If **there** was a competition, **whether** it was writing poems, designing a poster, or playing an instrument, you could be equally **sure** that Jake would win it.

Of course, the teachers loved Jake. **He** sat in class like an angel: listening carefully, answering questions, always handing in his homework on time. Jake would never be caught passing notes or poking someone else in the back when teacher wasn't looking. There was something that the teachers didn't know about Jake, though. Something which they would very much like to have known, although they might not have believed it.